www.EffortlessMath

... So Much More Online!

✓ FREE Math lessons

✓ More Math learning books!

✓ Mathematics Worksheets

✓ Online Math Tutors

Need a PDF version of this book?

Visit www.EffortlessMath.com

Or send email to: info@EffortlessMath.com

ASTB Math Prep 2020

A Comprehensive Review and Ultimate Guide to the ASTB-E Math Test

By

Reza Nazari & Ava Ross

Copyright © 2018

Reza Nazari & Ava Ross

All inquiries should be addressed to:

info@effortlessMath.com

www.EffortlessMath.com

ISBN-13: 978-1-64612-816-7

Published by: Effortless Math Education

www.EffortlessMath.com

Description

ASTB Math Prep 2020 provides students with the confidence and math skills they need to succeed on the ASTB-E Math, building a solid foundation of basic Math topics with abundant exercises for each topic. It is designed to address the needs of ASTB test takers who must have a working knowledge of basic Math.

This comprehensive book with over 2,500 sample questions and 10 complete ASTB Arithmetic Reasoning and Mathematics knowledge tests is all you need to fully prepare for the ASTB Math. It will help you learn everything you need to ace the math section of the ASTB.

Effortless Math unique study program provides you with an in-depth focus on the math portion of the test, helping you master the math skills that students find the most troublesome.

This book contains most common sample questions that are most likely to appear in the mathematics section of the ASTB-E.

Inside the pages of this comprehensive ASTB Math book, students can learn basic math operations in a structured manner with a complete study program to help them understand essential math skills. It also has many exciting features, including:

- Dynamic design and easy-to-follow activities
- A fun, interactive and concrete learning process
- Targeted, skill-building practices
- Fun exercises that build confidence
- Math topics are grouped by category, so you can focus on the topics you struggle on
- All solutions for the exercises are included, so you will always find the answers
- 10 Complete ASTB Math Practice Tests that reflect the format and question types on ASTB

ASTB Math Prep 2020 is an incredibly useful tool for those who want to review all topics being covered on the ASTB test. It efficiently and effectively reinforces learning outcomes through engaging questions and repeated practice, helping you to quickly master basic Math skills.

About the Author

Reza Nazari is the author of more than 100 Math learning books including:
– **Math and Critical Thinking Challenges:** For the Middle and High School Student
– **GED Math in 30 Days**
– **ASVAB Math Workbook 2018 - 2019**
– **Effortless Math Education Workbooks**
– **and many more Mathematics books …**

Reza is also an experienced Math instructor and a test–prep expert who has been tutoring students since 2008. Reza is the founder of Effortless Math Education, a tutoring company that has helped many students raise their standardized test scores—and attend the colleges of their dreams. Reza provides an individualized custom learning plan and the personalized attention that makes a difference in how students view math.

You can contact Reza via email at:
reza@EffortlessMath.com

Find Reza's professional profile at:
goo.gl/zoC9rJ

Contents

Chapter 1: Whole Numbers

Topics that you'll learn in this chapter:

- ✓ Place Value
- ✓ Rounding
- ✓ Whole Number Addition and Subtraction
- ✓ Whole Number Multiplication and Division
- ✓ Rounding and Estimates
- ✓ Comparing Numbers

"If people do not believe that mathematics is simple, it is only because they do not realize how complicated life is." — John von Neumann

Place Value

Helpful

Hints

The value of the place, or position, of a digit in a number.
For the number 3,684.26

Decimal Place Value Chart

Millions	Hundred thousands	Ten thousands	Thousands	Hundreds	Tens	Ones	Decimal point	Tenths	Hundredths	Thousandths	Ten-thousandths	Hundred thousandths	Millionths
			3	6	8	4	.	2	6				

Example:

In 456, the 5 is in "tens" position.

✎ *Write each number in expanded form.*

1) Thirty–five   30 + 5

2) Sixty–seven   ___ + ___

3) Forty–two   ___ + ___

4) Eighty–nine   ___ + ___

5) Ninety–one   ___ + ___

✎ *Circle the correct one.*

6)   The 2 in 72 is in the   ones place   tens place   hundreds place

7)   The 6 in 65 is in the   ones place   tens place   hundreds place

8)   The 2 in 342 is in the   ones place   tens place   hundreds place

9)   The 5 in 450 is in the   ones place   tens place   hundreds place

10)   The 3 in 321 is in the   ones place   tens place   hundreds place

Rounding

Helpful	— Rounding is putting a number up or down to the nearest whole number or the nearest hundred, etc.	**Example:**
Hints		64 rounded to the nearest ten is 60, because 64 is closer to 60 than to 70.

✍ *Round each number to the underlined place value.*

1) 9̲72

2) 2,9̲95

3) 36̲4

4) 8̲1

5) 5̲5

6) 33̲4

7) 1,2̲03

8) 9.5̲7

9) 7.4̲84

10) 9.1̲4

11) 3̲9

12) 9̲,123

13) 3,45̲2

14) 5̲69

15) 1,2̲30

16) 9̲8

17) 9̲3

18) 3̲7

19) 49̲3

20) 2,9̲23

21) 9̲,845

22) 55̲5

23) 9̲39

24) 6̲9

Whole Number Addition and Subtraction

Helpful *Hints*	1– Line up the numbers. 2– Start with the unit place. (ones place) 3– Regroup if necessary. 4– Add or subtract the tens place. 5– Continue with other digits.	**Example:** 231 + 120 = 351 292 – 90 = 202

✎ *Solve.*

1) A school had 891 students last year. If all last year students and 338 new students have registered for this year, how many students will there be in total?

2) Alice has just started her first job after graduating from college. Her yearly income is $33,000 per year. Alice's father income is $56,000 per year and her mother's income is $49,000. What is yearly income of Alice and her parent altogether?

3) Tom had $895 dollars in his saving account. He gave $235 dollars to his sister, Lisa. How much money does he have left?

4) Emily has 830 marbles, Daniel has 970 marbles, and Ethan has 230 marbles less than Daniel. How many marbles do they have in all?

✎ *Find the missing number.*

5) 890 – .... = 300

6) 1000 – .... = 200

7) .... – 4000 = 92000

8) 60000 – 51000 = ...

9) 3400 – .... = 3200

10) 33000 – 5000 = ...

Whole Number Multiplication and Division

Helpful **Hints**	**Multiplication:** − Learn the times tables first! − For multiplication, line up the numbers you are multiplying. − Start with the ones place. − Continue with other digits − A typical division problem: Dividend ÷ Divisor = Quotient **Division:** − In division, we want to find how many times a number (divisor) is contained in another number (dividend). − The result in a division problem is the quotient.	**Example:** $200 \times 90 = 18{,}000$ $18{,}000 \div 90 = 200$

✎ **Multiply and divided.**

1) $340 \div 8 =$

2) $1800 \div 20 =$

3) $50000 \div 10 =$

4) $966 \div 30 =$

5) $201 \times 20 =$

6) $400 \times 50 =$

7) $400 \times 90 =$

8) $888 \times 90 =$

9) $80 \times 80 =$

10) $122 \times 12 =$

11) $609 \times 8 =$

12) $220 \times 12 =$

13) A group of 235 students has collected \$8,565 for charity during last month. They decided to split the money evenly among 5 charities. How much will each charity receive?

14) Maria and her two brothers have 9 boxes of crayons. Each box contains 56 crayons. How many crayons do Maria and her two brothers have?

Rounding and Estimates

Helpful	— Rounding and estimating are math strategies used for approximating a number.	**Example:**
Hints	— To estimate means to make a rough guess or calculation.	$73 + 69 \approx 140$
	— To round means to simplify a known number by scaling it slightly up or down.	

✏️ *Estimate the sum by rounding each added to the nearest ten.*

1) 55 + 9

2) 25 + 12

3) 83 + 7

4) 32 + 37

5) 13 + 74

6) 34 + 11

7) 39 + 77

8) 25 + 4

9) 61 + 73

10) 64 + 59

11) 14 + 68

12) 82 + 12

13) 43 + 66

14) 45 + 65

15) 553 + 232

16) 418 + 846

17) 582 + 277

18) 2771 + 1651

19) 7436 + 3575

20) 1542 + 8738

21) 3843 + 6579

22) 4722 + 8186

23) 2419 + 7224

24) 6768 + 3169

Comparing Numbers

Helpful	Comparing:	Example:
	Equal to =	
Hints	Less than <	56 > 35
	Greater than >	
	Greater than or equal ≥	
	Less than or equal ≤	

✍ *Use > = <.*

1)	35	67	8)	90	56
2)	89	56	9)	94	98
3)	56	35	10)	48	23
4)	27	56	11)	24	54
5)	34	34	12)	89	89
6)	28	45	13)	50	30
7)	89	67	14)	20	20

✍ *Use less than, equal to or greater than.*

15) 23 _____ 34

16) 89 _____ 98

17) 45 _____ 25

18) 34 _____ 32

19) 91 _____ 91

20) 57 _____ 55

21) 85 _____ 78

22) 56 _____ 43

23) 34 _____ 34

24) 92 _____ 98

25) 38 _____ 46

26) 67 _____ 58

27) 88 _____ 69

28) 23 _____ 34

Answers of Worksheets – Chapter 1

Place Value

1) 30 + 5
2) 60 + 7
3) 40 + 2
4) 80 + 9
5) 90 + 1
6) ones place
7) tens place
8) ones place
9) tens place
10) hundreds place

Rounding

1) 1000
2) 3000
3) 360
4) 80
5) 60
6) 330
7) 1200
8) 9.6
9) 7.5
10) 9.1
11) 40
12) 9000
13) 3,450
14) 600
15) 1,200
16) 100
17) 90
18) 40
19) 490
20) 2,900
21) 10,000
22) 560
23) 900
24) 70

Whole Number Addition and Subtraction

1) 1229
2) 138000
3) 660
4) 2540
5) 590
6) 800
7) 96000
8) 9000
9) 200
10) 28000

Whole Number Multiplication and Division

1) 42.5
2) 90
3) 5000
4) 32.2
5) 4020
6) 20000
7) 36000
8) 79920
9) 6400
10) 1464
11) 4872
12) 2640
13) 1713
14) 504

Rounding and Estimates

1) 70	9) 130	17) 860
2) 40	10) 120	18) 4420
3) 90	11) 80	19) 11020
4) 70	12) 90	20) 10280
5) 37	13) 110	21) 10420
6) 40	14) 120	22) 12910
7) 120	15) 780	23) 9640
8) 30	16) 1270	24) 9940

Comparing Numbers

1) 35 < 67	15) 23 less than 34
2) 89 > 56	16) 89 less than 98
3) 56 > 35	17) 45 greater than 25
4) 27< 56	18) 34 greater than 32
5) 34 = 34	19) 91 equal to 91
6) 28 < 45	20) 57 greater than 55
7) 89 > 67	21) 85 greater than 78
8) 90 > 56	22) 56 greater than 43
9) 94 < 98	23) 34 equal to 34
10) 48 > 23	24) 92 less than 98
11) 24 < 54	25) 38 less than 46
12) 89 = 89	26) 67 greater than 58
13) 50 > 30	27) 88 greater than 69
14) 20 = 20	28) 23 less than 34

Chapter 2: Fractions and Decimals

Topics that you'll learn in this chapter:

- ✓ Simplifying Fractions
- ✓ Adding and Subtracting Fractions
- ✓ Multiplying and Dividing Fractions
- ✓ Adding Mixed Numbers
- ✓ Subtract Mixed Numbers
- ✓ Multiplying Mixed Numbers
- ✓ Dividing Mixed Numbers
- ✓ Comparing Decimals
- ✓ Rounding Decimals
- ✓ Adding and Subtracting Decimals
- ✓ Multiplying and Dividing Decimals
- ✓ Converting Between Fractions, Decimals and Mixed Numbers
- ✓ Factoring Numbers
- ✓ Greatest Common Factor
- ✓ Least Common Multiple
- ✓ Divisibility Rules

"A Man is like a fraction whose numerator is what he is and whose denominator is what he thinks of himself. The larger the denominator, the smaller the fraction." –Tolstoy

Simplifying Fractions

Helpful	– Evenly divide both the top and bottom of the fraction by 2, 3, 5, 7, ... etc.	**Example:**
Hints	– Continue until you can't go any further.	$\dfrac{4}{12} = \dfrac{2}{6} = \dfrac{1}{3}$

✍️ *Simplify the fractions.*

1) $\dfrac{22}{36}$

2) $\dfrac{8}{10}$

3) $\dfrac{12}{18}$

4) $\dfrac{6}{8}$

5) $\dfrac{13}{39}$

6) $\dfrac{5}{20}$

7) $\dfrac{16}{36}$

8) $\dfrac{18}{36}$

9) $\dfrac{20}{50}$

10) $\dfrac{6}{54}$

11) $\dfrac{45}{81}$

12) $\dfrac{21}{28}$

13) $\dfrac{35}{56}$

14) $\dfrac{52}{64}$

15) $\dfrac{13}{65}$

16) $\dfrac{44}{77}$

17) $\dfrac{21}{42}$

18) $\dfrac{15}{36}$

19) $\dfrac{9}{24}$

20) $\dfrac{20}{80}$

21) $\dfrac{25}{45}$

Adding and Subtracting Fractions

Helpful

Hints

– For "like" fractions (fractions with the same denominator), add or subtract the numerators and write the answer over the common denominator.
– Find equivalent fractions with the same denominator before you can add or subtract fractions with different denominators.
– Adding and Subtracting with the same denominator:

$$\frac{a}{b} + \frac{c}{b} = \frac{a+c}{b}$$

$$\frac{a}{b} - \frac{c}{b} = \frac{a-c}{b}$$

– Adding and Subtracting fractions with different denominators:

$$\frac{a}{b} + \frac{c}{d} = \frac{ad+cb}{bd}$$

$$\frac{a}{b} - \frac{c}{d} = \frac{ad-cb}{bd}$$

✍ Add fractions.

1) $\frac{2}{3} + \frac{1}{2}$

2) $\frac{3}{5} + \frac{1}{3}$

3) $\frac{5}{6} + \frac{1}{2}$

4) $\frac{7}{4} + \frac{5}{9}$

5) $\frac{2}{5} + \frac{1}{5}$

6) $\frac{3}{7} + \frac{1}{2}$

7) $\frac{3}{4} + \frac{2}{5}$

8) $\frac{2}{3} + \frac{1}{5}$

9) $\frac{16}{25} + \frac{3}{5}$

✍ Subtract fractions.

10) $\frac{4}{5} - \frac{2}{5}$

11) $\frac{3}{5} - \frac{2}{7}$

12) $\frac{1}{2} - \frac{1}{3}$

13) $\frac{8}{9} - \frac{3}{5}$

14) $\frac{3}{7} - \frac{3}{14}$

15) $\frac{4}{15} - \frac{1}{10}$

16) $\frac{3}{4} - \frac{13}{18}$

17) $\frac{5}{8} - \frac{2}{5}$

18) $\frac{1}{2} - \frac{1}{9}$

Multiplying and Dividing Fractions

Helpful *Hints*	– **Multiplying fractions:** multiply the top numbers and multiply the bottom numbers. – **Dividing fractions:** Keep, Change, Flip Keep first fraction, change division sign to multiplication, and flip the numerator and denominator of the second fraction. Then, solve!	**Example:** $\dfrac{a}{b} \times \dfrac{c}{d} = \dfrac{a \times c}{b \times d}$ $\dfrac{a}{b} \div \dfrac{c}{d} = \dfrac{a}{b} \times \dfrac{d}{c} = \dfrac{ad}{bc}$

✎ *Multiplying fractions. Then simplify.*

1) $\dfrac{1}{5} \times \dfrac{2}{3}$ 4) $\dfrac{3}{8} \times \dfrac{1}{3}$ 7) $\dfrac{2}{3} \times \dfrac{3}{8}$

2) $\dfrac{3}{4} \times \dfrac{2}{3}$ 5) $\dfrac{3}{5} \times \dfrac{2}{5}$ 8) $\dfrac{1}{4} \times \dfrac{1}{3}$

3) $\dfrac{2}{5} \times \dfrac{3}{7}$ 6) $\dfrac{7}{9} \times \dfrac{1}{3}$ 9) $\dfrac{5}{7} \times \dfrac{7}{12}$

✎ *Dividing fractions.*

10) $\dfrac{2}{9} \div \dfrac{1}{4}$ 13) $\dfrac{11}{14} \div \dfrac{1}{10}$ 16) $\dfrac{3}{5} \div \dfrac{1}{5}$

11) $\dfrac{1}{2} \div \dfrac{1}{3}$ 14) $\dfrac{3}{5} \div \dfrac{5}{9}$ 17) $\dfrac{12}{21} \div \dfrac{3}{7}$

12) $\dfrac{6}{11} \div \dfrac{3}{4}$ 15) $\dfrac{1}{2} \div \dfrac{1}{2}$ 18) $\dfrac{5}{14} \div \dfrac{9}{10}$

Adding Mixed Numbers

Helpful	Use the following steps for both adding and subtracting mixed numbers.	**Example:**
Hints	– Find the Least Common Denominator (LCD) – Find the equivalent fractions for each mixed number. – Add fractions after finding common denominator. – Write your answer in lowest terms.	$1\frac{3}{4} + 2\frac{3}{8} = 4\frac{1}{8}$

✎ **Add.**

1) $4\frac{1}{2} + 5\frac{1}{2}$

2) $2\frac{3}{8} + 3\frac{1}{8}$

3) $6\frac{1}{5} + 3\frac{2}{5}$

4) $1\frac{1}{3} + 2\frac{2}{3}$

5) $5\frac{1}{6} + 5\frac{1}{2}$

6) $3\frac{1}{3} + 1\frac{1}{3}$

7) $1\frac{10}{11} + 1\frac{1}{3}$

8) $2\frac{3}{6} + 1\frac{1}{2}$

9) $5\frac{3}{5} + 5\frac{1}{5}$

10) $7 + \frac{1}{5}$

11) $1\frac{5}{7} + \frac{1}{3}$

12) $2\frac{1}{4} + 1\frac{1}{2}$

Subtract Mixed Numbers

Helpful	Use the following steps for both adding and subtracting mixed numbers.	**Example:**
Hints	Find the Least Common Denominator (LCD) — Find the equivalent fractions for each mixed number. — Add or subtract fractions after finding common denominator. — Write your answer in lowest terms.	$5\frac{2}{3} - 3\frac{2}{7} = 2\frac{8}{21}$

✎ *Subtract.*

1) $4\frac{1}{2} - 3\frac{1}{2}$

2) $3\frac{3}{8} - 3\frac{1}{8}$

3) $6\frac{3}{5} - 5\frac{1}{5}$

4) $2\frac{1}{3} - 1\frac{2}{3}$

5) $6\frac{1}{6} - 5\frac{1}{2}$

6) $3\frac{1}{3} - 1\frac{1}{3}$

7) $2\frac{10}{11} - 1\frac{1}{3}$

8) $2\frac{1}{2} - 1\frac{1}{2}$

9) $6\frac{3}{5} - 2\frac{1}{5}$

10) $7\frac{2}{5} - 1\frac{1}{5}$

11) $2\frac{5}{7} - 1\frac{1}{3}$

12) $2\frac{1}{4} - 1\frac{1}{2}$

Multiplying Mixed Numbers

Helpful	1- Convert the mixed numbers to improper fractions.	**Example:**
Hints	2- Multiply fractions and simplify if necessary. $$a\frac{c}{b} = a + \frac{c}{b} = \frac{ab\ \ c}{b}$$	$$2\frac{1}{3} \times 5\frac{3}{7} =$$ $$\frac{7}{3} \times \frac{38}{7} = \frac{38}{3} = 12\frac{2}{3}$$

✐ **Find each product.**

1) $1\frac{2}{3} \times 1\frac{1}{4}$

2) $1\frac{3}{5} \times 1\frac{2}{3}$

3) $1\frac{2}{3} \times 3\frac{2}{7}$

4) $4\frac{1}{8} \times 1\frac{2}{5}$

5) $2\frac{2}{5} \times 3\frac{1}{5}$

6) $1\frac{1}{3} \times 1\frac{2}{3}$

7) $1\frac{5}{8} \times 2\frac{1}{2}$

8) $3\frac{2}{5} \times 2\frac{1}{5}$

9) $2\frac{2}{3} \times 4\frac{1}{4}$

10) $2\frac{3}{5} \times 1\frac{2}{4}$

11) $1\frac{1}{3} \times 1\frac{1}{4}$

12) $3\frac{2}{5} \times 1\frac{1}{5}$

Dividing Mixed Numbers

Helpful

Hints

1- Convert the mixed numbers to improper fractions.
2- Divide fractions and simplify if necessary.

$$a\frac{c}{b} = a + \frac{c}{b} = \frac{ab+c}{b}$$

Example:

$$10\frac{1}{2} \div 5\frac{3}{5} =$$

$$\frac{21}{2} \div \frac{28}{5} = \frac{21}{2} \times \frac{5}{28} = \frac{105}{56}$$

$$= 1\frac{7}{8}$$

✎ *Find each quotient.*

1) $2\frac{1}{5} \div 2\frac{1}{2}$

2) $2\frac{3}{5} \div 1\frac{1}{3}$

3) $3\frac{1}{6} \div 4\frac{2}{3}$

4) $1\frac{2}{3} \div 3\frac{1}{3}$

5) $4\frac{1}{8} \div 2\frac{2}{4}$

6) $3\frac{1}{2} \div 2\frac{3}{5}$

7) $3\frac{5}{9} \div 1\frac{2}{5}$

8) $2\frac{2}{7} \div 1\frac{1}{2}$

9) $3\frac{1}{5} \div 1\frac{1}{2}$

10) $4\frac{3}{5} \div 2\frac{1}{3}$

11) $6\frac{1}{6} \div 1\frac{2}{3}$

12) $2\frac{2}{3} \div 1\frac{1}{3}$

Comparing Decimals

Helpful Hints	- **Decimals:** is a fraction written in a special form. For example, instead of writing $\frac{1}{2}$ you can write 0.5. - **For comparing:** Equal to = Less than < Greater than > Greater than or equal ≥ Less than or equal ≤	**Example:** 2.67 > 0.267

✎ *Write the correct comparison symbol (>, < or =).*

1) 1.25   2.3

2) 0.5   0.23

3) 3.2   3.2

4) 4.58   45.8

5) 2.75   0.275

6) 5.2   5

7) 3.1   0.31

8) 6.33   0.733

9) 8   0.8

10) 4.56 0.456

11) 1.12 1.14

12) 2.77 2.78

13) 6.08 6.11

14) 1.11 0.211

15) 2.6   2.55

16) 1.24 1.25

17) 5.52 0.552

18) 0.33 0.033

19) 14.4 14.4

20) 0.05 0.50

21) 0.59 0.7

22) 0.5   0.05

23) 0.90 0.9

24) 0.27 0.4

Rounding Decimals

Helpful	We can round decimals to a certain accuracy or number of decimal places. This is used to make calculation easier to do and results easier to understand, when exact values are not too important.	Example:
		$\underline{6}.37 = 6$
Hints	First, you'll need to remember your place values:	

12.4567

1: tens	2: ones	4: tenths
5: hundredths	6: thousandths	7: tens thousandths

✏ *Round each decimal number to the nearest place indicated.*

1) 0.2̲3

2) 4.0̲4

3) 5.6̲23

4) 0.2̲66

5) 6̲.37

6) 0.8̲8

7) 8.2̲4

8) 7̲.0760

9) 1.62̲9

10) 6.3̲959

11) 1̲.9

12) 5̲.2167

13) 5.8̲63

14) 8.5̲4

15) 80̲.69

16) 65̲.85

17) 70.7̲8

18) 615̲.755

19) 16̲.4

20) 95̲.81

21) 2̲.408

22) 76̲.3

23) 116.5̲14

24) 8.0̲6

Adding and Subtracting Decimals

Helpful	1– Line up the numbers.	Example:
	2– Add zeros to have same number of digits for both numbers.	16.18
Hints		$-\ 13.45$
	3– Add or Subtract using column addition or subtraction.	2.73

✎ *Add and subtract decimals.*

1) $\begin{array}{r} 15.14 \\ -\ 12.18 \\ \hline \end{array}$

3) $\begin{array}{r} 82.56 \\ +\ 12.28 \\ \hline \end{array}$

5) $\begin{array}{r} 90.37 \\ +\ 56.97 \\ \hline \end{array}$

2) $\begin{array}{r} 65.72 \\ +\ 43.67 \\ \hline \end{array}$

4) $\begin{array}{r} 34.18 \\ -\ 23.45 \\ \hline \end{array}$

6) $\begin{array}{r} 45.78 \\ -\ 23.39 \\ \hline \end{array}$

✎ *Solve.*

7) ____ + 1.3 = 4.8

10) 6.9 + ____ = 16.4

8) 4.2 + ____ = 11.6

11) ____ + 5.1 = 8.6

9) 9.9 + ____ = 16

12) ____ + 7.9 = 15.2

Multiplying and Dividing Decimals

Helpful	**For Multiplication:**
	– Set up and multiply the numbers as you do with whole numbers.
Hints	– Count the total number of decimal places in both of the factors.
	– Place the decimal point in the product.
	For Division:
	– If the divisor is not a whole number, move decimal point to right to make it a whole number. Do the same for dividend.
	– Divide similar to whole numbers.

✏ *Find each product.*

1)
$\quad\quad 4.5$
$\times\ 1.6$
———

2)
$\quad\quad 7.7$
$\times\ 9.9$
———

3)
$\quad\quad 2.6$
$\times\ 1.5$
———

4)
$\quad\quad 8.9$
$\times\ 9.7$
———

5)
$\quad\quad 15.1$
$\times\ 12.6$
———

6)
$\quad\quad 6.9$
$\times\ 3.3$
———

7)
$\quad\quad 5.7$
$\times\ 7.8$
———

8)
$\quad\quad 98.20$
$\times\ 100$
———

9)
$\quad\quad 23.99$
$\times\ 1000$
———

✏ *Find each quotient.*

10) $9.2 \div 3.6$

11) $27.6 \div 3.8$

12) $12.6 \div 4.7$

13) $6.5 \div 8.1$

14) $1.4 \div 10$

15) $3.6 \div 100$

16) $4.24 \div 10$

17) $14.6 \div 100$

18) $1.8 \div 1000$

Converting Between Fractions, Decimals and Mixed Numbers

Helpful	**Fraction to Decimal:**
	– Divide the top number by the bottom number.
Hints	**Decimal to Fraction:**
	– Write decimal over 1.
	– Multiply both top and bottom by 10 for every digit on the right side of the decimal point.
	– Simplify.

✍ *Convert fractions to decimals.*

1) $\dfrac{9}{10}$

2) $\dfrac{56}{100}$

3) $\dfrac{3}{4}$

4) $\dfrac{2}{5}$

5) $\dfrac{3}{9}$

6) $\dfrac{40}{50}$

7) $\dfrac{12}{10}$

8) $\dfrac{8}{5}$

9) $\dfrac{69}{10}$

✍ *Convert decimal into fraction or mixed numbers.*

10) 0.3

11) 4.5

12) 2.5

13) 2.3

14) 0.8

15) 0.25

16) 0.14

17) 0.2

18) 0.08

19) 0.45

20) 2.6

21) 5.2

Factoring Numbers

Helpful	- Factoring numbers means to break the numbers into their prime factors.	**Example:**
Hints	- First few prime numbers: 2, 3, 5, 7, 11, 13, 17, 19	$12 = 2 \times 2 \times 3$

✍ List all positive factors of each number.

1) 68

2) 56

3) 24

4) 40

5) 86

6) 78

7) 50

8) 98

9) 45

10) 26

11) 54

12) 28

13) 55

14) 85

15) 48

✍ List the prime factorization for each number.

16) 50

17) 25

18) 69

19) 21

20) 45

21) 68

22) 26

23) 86

24) 93

Greatest Common Factor

Helpful		
	- List the prime factors of each number.	**Example:**
Hints	- Multiply common prime factors.	
		$200 = 2 \times 2 \times 2 \times 5 \times 5$
		$60 = 2 \times 2 \times 3 \times 5$
		GCF $(200, 60) = 2 \times 2 \times 5 = 20$

✎ *Find the GCF for each number pair.*

1) 20, 30

2) 4, 14

3) 5, 45

4) 68, 12

5) 5, 12

6) 15, 27

7) 3, 24

8) 34, 6

9) 4, 10

10) 5, 3

11) 6, 16

12) 30, 3

13) 24, 28

14) 70, 10

15) 45, 8

16) 90, 35

17) 78, 34

18) 55, 75

19) 60, 72

20) 100, 78

21) 30, 40

Least Common Multiple

Helpful *Hints*	- Find the GCF for the two numbers. - Divide that GCF into either number. - Take that answer and multiply it by the other number.	**Example:** LCM (200, 60): GCF is 20 $200 \div 20 = 10$ $10 \times 60 = 600$

✎ *Find the LCM for each number pair.*

1) 4, 14

2) 5, 15

3) 16, 10

4) 4, 34

5) 8, 3

6) 12, 24

7) 9, 18

8) 5, 6

9) 8, 19

10) 9, 21

11) 19, 29

12) 7, 6

13) 25, 6

14) 4, 8

15) 30, 10, 50

16) 18, 36, 27

17) 12, 8, 18

18) 8, 18, 4

19) 26, 20, 30

20) 10, 4, 24

21) 15, 30, 45

Divisibility Rules

Helpful	-	Divisibility means that a number can be divided by other numbers evenly.	**Example:** 24 is divisible by 6, because 24 ÷ 6 = 4
Hints			

✎ *Use the divisibility rules to find the factors of each number.*

	8	<u>2</u> 3 <u>4</u> 5 6 7 <u>8</u> 9 10
1)	16	2 3 4 5 6 7 8 9 10
2)	10	2 3 4 5 6 7 8 9 10
3)	15	2 3 4 5 6 7 8 9 10
4)	28	2 3 4 5 6 7 8 9 10
5)	36	2 3 4 5 6 7 8 9 10
6)	15	2 3 4 5 6 7 8 9 10
7)	27	2 3 4 5 6 7 8 9 10
8)	70	2 3 4 5 6 7 8 9 10
9)	57	2 3 4 5 6 7 8 9 10
10)	102	2 3 4 5 6 7 8 9 10
11)	144	2 3 4 5 6 7 8 9 10
12)	75	2 3 4 5 6 7 8 9 10

Answers of Worksheets – Chapter 2

Simplifying Fractions

1) $\dfrac{11}{18}$

2) $\dfrac{4}{5}$

3) $\dfrac{2}{3}$

4) $\dfrac{3}{4}$

5) $\dfrac{1}{3}$

6) $\dfrac{1}{4}$

7) $\dfrac{4}{9}$

8) $\dfrac{1}{2}$

9) $\dfrac{2}{5}$

10) $\dfrac{1}{9}$

11) $\dfrac{5}{9}$

12) $\dfrac{3}{4}$

13) $\dfrac{5}{8}$

14) $\dfrac{13}{16}$

15) $\dfrac{1}{5}$

16) $\dfrac{4}{7}$

17) $\dfrac{1}{2}$

18) $\dfrac{5}{12}$

19) $\dfrac{3}{8}$

20) $\dfrac{1}{4}$

21) $\dfrac{5}{9}$

Adding and Subtracting Fractions

1) $\dfrac{7}{6}$

2) $\dfrac{14}{15}$

3) $\dfrac{4}{3}$

4) $\dfrac{83}{36}$

5) $\dfrac{3}{5}$

6) $\dfrac{13}{14}$

7) $\dfrac{23}{20}$

8) $\dfrac{13}{15}$

9) $\dfrac{31}{25}$

10) $\dfrac{2}{5}$

11) $\dfrac{11}{35}$

12) $\dfrac{1}{6}$

13) $\dfrac{13}{45}$

14) $\dfrac{3}{14}$

15) $\dfrac{1}{6}$

16) $\dfrac{1}{36}$

17) $\dfrac{9}{40}$

18) $\dfrac{7}{18}$

Multiplying and Dividing Fractions

1) $\frac{2}{15}$

2) $\frac{1}{2}$

3) $\frac{6}{35}$

4) $\frac{1}{8}$

5) $\frac{6}{25}$

6) $\frac{7}{27}$

7) $\frac{1}{4}$

8) $\frac{1}{12}$

9) $\frac{5}{12}$

10) $\frac{8}{9}$

11) $\frac{3}{2}$

12) $\frac{8}{11}$

13) $\frac{55}{7}$

14) $\frac{27}{25}$

15) 1

16) 3

17) $\frac{4}{3}$

18) $\frac{25}{63}$

Adding Mixed Numbers

1) 10

2) $5\frac{1}{2}$

3) $9\frac{3}{5}$

4) 4

5) $10\frac{2}{3}$

6) $4\frac{2}{3}$

7) $3\frac{8}{33}$

8) 4

9) $10\frac{4}{5}$

10) $7\frac{1}{5}$

11) $2\frac{1}{21}$

12) $3\frac{3}{4}$

Subtract Mixed Numbers

1) 1

2) $\frac{1}{4}$

3) $1\frac{2}{5}$

4) $\frac{2}{3}$

5) $\frac{2}{3}$

6) 2

7) $1\frac{19}{33}$

8) 1

9) $4\frac{2}{5}$

10) $6\frac{1}{5}$

11) $1\frac{8}{21}$

12) $\frac{3}{4}$

Multiplying Mixed Numbers

1) $2\frac{1}{12}$

2) $2\frac{2}{3}$

3) $5\frac{10}{21}$

4) $5\frac{31}{40}$

5) $7\frac{17}{25}$

6) $2\frac{2}{9}$

7) $4\frac{1}{16}$

8) $7\frac{12}{25}$

9) $11\frac{1}{3}$

10) $3\frac{9}{10}$

11) $1\frac{2}{3}$

12) $4\frac{2}{25}$

Dividing Mixed Numbers

1) $\frac{22}{25}$

2) $1\frac{19}{20}$

3) $\frac{19}{28}$

4) $\frac{1}{2}$

5) $1\frac{13}{20}$

6) $1\frac{9}{26}$

7) $2\frac{34}{63}$

8) $1\frac{11}{21}$

9) $2\frac{2}{15}$

10) $1\frac{34}{35}$

11) $3\frac{7}{10}$

12) 2

Comparing Decimals

1) $1.25 < 2.3$

2) $0.5 > 0.23$

3) $3.2 = 3.2$

4) $4.58 < 45.8$

5) $2.75 > 0.275$

6) $5.2 > 5$

7) $3.1 > 0.31$

8) $6.33 > 0.733$

9) $8 > 0.8$

10) $4.56 > 0.456$

11) $1.12 < 1.14$

12) $2.77 < 2.78$

13) $6.08 < 6.11$

14) $1.11 > 0.211$

15) $2.6 > 2.55$

16) $1.24 < 1.25$

17) $5.52 > 0.552$

18) $0.33 > 0.033$

19) $14.4 = 14.4$

20) $0.05 < 0.50$

21) $0.59 < 0.7$

22) $0.5 > 0.05$

23) $0.90 = 0.9$

24) $0.27 < 0.4$

Rounding Decimals

1) 0.2	9) 1.63	17) 70.8
2) 4.0	10) 6.4	18) 616
3) 5.6	11) 2	19) 16
4) 0.3	12) 5	20) 96
5) 6	13) 5.9	21) 2
6) 0.9	14) 8.5	22) 76
7) 8.2	15) 81	23) 116.5
8) 7	16) 66	24) 8.1

Adding and Subtracting Decimals

1) 2.96	5) 147.34	9) 6.1
2) 109.39	6) 22.39	10) 9.5
3) 94.84	7) 3.5	11) 3.5
4) 10.73	8) 7.4	12) 7.3

Multiplying and Dividing Decimals

1) 7.2	7) 44.46	13) 0.8024…
2) 76.23	8) 9820	14) 0.14
3) 3.9	9) 23990	15) 0.036
4) 86.33	10) 2.5555…	16) 0.424
5) 190.26	11) 7.2631…	17) 0.146
6) 22.77	12) 2.6808…	18) 0.0018

Converting Between Fractions, Decimals and Mixed Numbers

1) 0.9	7) 1.2	12) $2\frac{1}{2}$
2) 0.56	8) 1.6	13) $2\frac{3}{10}$
3) 0.75	9) 6.9	14) $\frac{4}{5}$
4) 0.4	10) $\frac{3}{10}$	15) $\frac{1}{4}$
5) 0.333…	11) $4\frac{1}{2}$	
6) 0.8		

16) $\dfrac{7}{50}$ 18) $\dfrac{2}{25}$ 20) $2\dfrac{3}{5}$

17) $\dfrac{1}{5}$ 19) $\dfrac{9}{20}$ 21) $5\dfrac{1}{5}$

Factoring Numbers

1) 1, 2, 4, 17, 34, 68
2) 1, 2, 4, 7, 8, 14, 28, 56
3) 1, 2, 3, 4, 6, 8, 12, 24
4) 1, 2, 4, 5, 8, 10, 20, 40
5) 1, 2, 43, 86
6) 1, 2, 3, 6, 13, 26, 39, 78
7) 1, 2, 5, 10, 25, 50
8) 1, 2, 7, 14, 49, 98
9) 1, 3, 5, 9, 15, 45
10) 1, 2, 13, 26
11) 1, 2, 3, 6, 9, 18, 27, 54
12) 1, 2, 4, 7, 14, 28

13) 1, 5, 11, 55
14) 1, 5, 17, 85
15) 1, 2, 3, 4, 6, 8, 12, 16, 24, 48
16) $2 \times 5 \times 5$
17) 5×5
18) 3×23
19) 3×7
20) $3 \times 3 \times 5$
21) $2 \times 2 \times 17$
22) 2×13
23) 2×43
24) 3×31

Greatest Common Factor

1) 10
2) 2
3) 5
4) 4
5) 1
6) 3
7) 3

8) 2
9) 2
10) 1
11) 2
12) 3
13) 4
14) 10

15) 1
16) 5
17) 2
18) 5
19) 12
20) 2
21) 10

Least Common Multiple

1) 28
2) 15
3) 80
4) 68
5) 24
6) 24
7) 18

8) 30
9) 152
10) 63
11) 551
12) 42
13) 150
14) 8

15) 150
16) 108
17) 72
18) 72
19) 780
20) 120
21) 90

Divisibility Rules

1) 16   <u>2</u> 3 <u>4</u> 5 6 7 <u>8</u> 9 10

2) 10   <u>2</u> 3 4 <u>5</u> 6 7 8 9 <u>10</u>

3) 15   2 <u>3</u> 4 <u>5</u> 6 7 8 9 10

4) 28   <u>2</u> 3 <u>4</u> 5 6 <u>7</u> 8 9 10

5) 36   <u>2</u> <u>3</u> <u>4</u> 5 <u>6</u> 7 8 <u>9</u> 10

6) 18   <u>2</u> <u>3</u> 4 5 <u>6</u> 7 8 <u>9</u> 10

7) 27   2 <u>3</u> 4 5 6 7 8 <u>9</u> 10

8) 70   <u>2</u> 3 4 <u>5</u> 6 <u>7</u> 8 9 <u>10</u>

9) 57   2 <u>3</u> 4 5 6 7 8 9 10

10) 102   <u>2</u> <u>3</u> 4 5 <u>6</u> 7 8 9 10

11) 144   <u>2</u> <u>3</u> <u>4</u> 5 <u>6</u> 7 <u>8</u> <u>9</u> 10

12) 75   2 <u>3</u> 4 <u>5</u> 6 7 8 9 10

Chapter 3: Real Numbers and Integers

Topics that you'll learn in this chapter:

✓ Adding and Subtracting Integers

✓ Multiplying and Dividing Integers

✓ Ordering Integers and Numbers

✓ Arrange and Order, Comparing Integers

✓ Order of Operations

✓ Mixed Integer Computations

✓ Integers and Absolute Value

"Wherever there is number, there is beauty." –Proclus

Adding and Subtracting Integers

Helpful		**Integers:** {… , −3, −2, −1, 0, 1, 2, 3, …} Includes: zero, counting numbers, and the negative of the counting numbers.	**Example:**
Hints		– Add a positive integer by moving to the right on the number line.	$12 + 10 = 22$ $25 − 13 = 12$
		– Add a negative integer by moving to the left on the number line.	$(−24) + 12 = −12$
		– Subtract an integer by adding its opposite.	$(−14) + (−12) = −26$ $14 − (−13) = 27$

✍ *Find the sum.*

1) $(−12) + (−4)$

2) $5 + (−24)$

3) $(−14) + 23$

4) $(−8) + (39)$

5) $43 + (−12)$

6) $(−23) + (−4) + 3$

7) $4 + (−12) + (−10) + (−25)$

8) $19 + (−15) + 25 + 11$

9) $(−9) + (−12) + (32 − 14)$

10) $4 + (−30) + (45 − 34)$

✍ *Find the difference.*

11) $(−14) − (−9) − (18)$

12) $(−9) − (−25)$

13) $(−12) − (8)$

14) $(28) − (−4)$

15) $(34) − (2)$

16) $(55) − (−5) + (−4)$

17) $(9) − (2) − (−5)$

18) $(2) − (4) − (−15)$

19) $(23) − (4) − (−34)$

20) $(−45) − (−87)$

Multiplying and Dividing Integers

Helpful	(negative) × (negative) = positive	**Examples:**
	(negative) ÷ (negative) = positive	$3 \times 2 = 6$
Hints	(negative) × (positive) = negative	$3 \times -3 = -9$
	(negative) ÷ (positive) = negative	$-2 \times -2 = 4$
	(positive) × (positive) = positive	$10 \div 2 = 5$
		$-4 \div 2 = -2$
		$-12 \div -6 = 3$

✎ *Find each product.*

1) $(-8) \times (-2)$

2) 3×6

3) $(-4) \times 5 \times (-6)$

4) $2 \times (-6) \times (-6)$

5) $11 \times (-12)$

6) $10 \times (-5)$

7) 8×8

8) $(-8) \times (-9)$

9) $6 \times (-5) \times 3$

10) $6 \times (-1) \times 2$

✎ *Find each quotient.*

11) $18 \div 3$

12) $(-24) \div 4$

13) $(-63) \div (-9)$

14) $54 \div 9$

15) $20 \div (-2)$

16) $(-66) \div (-11)$

17) $64 \div 8$

18) $(-121) \div 11$

19) $72 \div 9$

20) $16 \div 4$

Ordering Integers and Numbers

Helpful	To compare numbers, you can use number line! As you move from left to right on the number line, you find a bigger number!	**Example:**
Hints		Order integers from least to greatest.
		$(-11, -13, 7, -2, 12)$
		$-13 < -11 < -2 < 7 < 12$

✎ **Order each set of integers from least to greatest.**

1) $-15, -19, 20, -4, 1$ ___, ___, ___, ___, ___, ___

2) $6, -5, 4, -3, 2$ ___, ___, ___, ___, ___, ___

3) $15, -42, 19, 0, -22$ ___, ___, ___, ___, ___, ___

4) $26, -91, 0, -13, 67, -55$ ___, ___, ___, ___, ___, ___

5) $-17, -71, 90, -25, -54, -39$ ___, ___, ___, ___, ___, ___

6) $98, 5, 46, 19, 77, 24$ ___, ___, ___, ___, ___, ___

✎ **Order each set of integers from greatest to least.**

7) $-2, 5, -3, 6, -4$ ___, ___, ___, ___, ___, ___

8) $-37, 7, -17, 27, 47$ ___, ___, ___, ___, ___, ___

9) $32, -27, 19, -17, 15$ ___, ___, ___, ___, ___, ___

10) $68, 81, 21, -18, 94, 72$ ___, ___, ___, ___, ___, ___

Arrange, Order, and Comparing Integers

Helpful	When using a number line, numbers increase as you move to the right.	**Examples:**
Hints		$5 < 7$,
		$-5 < -2$
		$-18 < -12$

✎*Arrange these integers in descending order.*

1) $21, 71, -18, -10, 82$ ___, ___, ___, ___, ___, ___

2) $15, 11, 20, 12, -9, -5$ ___, ___, ___, ___, ___, ___

3) $-5, 20, 15, 9, -11$ ___, ___, ___, ___, ___, ___

4) $19, 18, -9, -6, -11$ ___, ___, ___, ___, ___, ___

5) $56, -34, -12, -5, 32$ ___, ___, ___, ___, ___, ___

✎*Compare. Use >, =, <*

6) -8 ____ 12 11) -56 ____ -58

7) -10 ____ -16 12) 78 ____ 87

8) 43 ____ 34 13) -92 ____ -102

9) 15 ____ -16 14) -12 ____ -12

10) -354 ____ -345 15) -721 ____ -821

Order of Operations

Helpful	-	Use "order of operations" rule when there are more than one math operation.	**Example:**
Hints	-	PEMDAS (parentheses / exponents / multiply / divide / add / subtract)	$(12 + 4) \div (- 4) = - 4$

✎**Evaluate each expression.**

1) $(2 \times 2) + 5$

2) $24 - (3 \times 3)$

3) $(6 \times 4) + 8$

4) $25 - (4 \times 2)$

5) $(6 \times 5) + 3$

6) $64 - (2 \times 4)$

7) $25 + (1 \times 8)$

8) $(6 \times 7) + 7$

9) $48 \div (4 + 4)$

10) $(7 + 11) \div (- 2)$

11) $9 + (2 \times 5) + 10$

12) $(5 + 8) \times \dfrac{3}{5} + 2$

13) $2 \times 7 - (\dfrac{10}{9 - 4})$

14) $(12 + 2 - 5) \times 7 - 1$

15) $(\dfrac{7}{5 - 1}) \times (2 + 6) \times 2$

16) $20 \div (4 - (10 - 8))$

17) $\dfrac{50}{4\,(5 - 4) - 3}$

18) $2 + (8 \times 2)$

Mixed Integer Computations

Helpful	It worth remembering:	Example:
Helpful	(negative) × (negative) = positive	
	(negative) ÷ (negative) = positive	$(-5) + 6 = 1$
Hints	(negative) × (positive) = negative	$(-3) × (-2) = 6$
	(negative) ÷ (positive) = negative	$(9) ÷ (-3) = -3$
	(positive) × (positive) = positive	

✎ *Compute.*

1) $(-70) ÷ (-5)$

2) $(-14) × 3$

3) $(-4) × (-15)$

4) $(-65) ÷ 5$

5) $18 × (-7)$

6) $(-12) × (-2)$

7) $\dfrac{(-60)}{(-20)}$

8) $24 ÷ (-8)$

9) $22 ÷ (-11)$

10) $\dfrac{(-27)}{3}$

11) $4 × (-4)$

12) $\dfrac{(-48)}{12}$

13) $(-14) × (-2)$

14) $(-7) × (7)$

15) $\dfrac{-30}{-6}$

16) $(-54) ÷ 6$

17) $(-60) ÷ (-5)$

18) $(-7) × (-12)$

19) $(-14) × 5$

20) $88 ÷ (-8)$

Integers and Absolute Value

Helpful *Hints*	To find an absolute value of a number, just find it's distance from 0!	**Example:** $\|-6\| = 6$ $\|6\| = 6$ $\|-12\| = 12$ $\|12\| = 12$

✎ *Write absolute value of each number.*

1) -4

2) -7

3) -8

4) 4

5) 5

6) -10

7) 1

8) 6

9) 8

10) -2

11) -1

12) 10

13) 3

14) 7

15) -5

16) -3

17) -9

18) 2

19) 4

20) -6

21) 9

✎ *Evaluate.*

22) $\|-43\| - \|12\| + 10$

23) $76 + \|-15 - 45\| - \|3\|$

24) $30 + \|-62\| - 46$

25) $\|32\| - \|-78\| + 90$

26) $\|-35 + 4\| + 6 - 4$

27) $\|-4\| + \|-11\|$

28) $\|-6 + 3 - 4\| + \|7 + 7\|$

29) $\|-9\| + \|-19\| - 5$

Answers of Worksheets – CHAPTER 3

Adding and Subtracting Integers

1) − 16
2) − 19
3) 9
4) 31
5) 31
6) − 24
7) − 43

8) 40
9) − 3
10) − 15
11) − 23
12) 16
13) − 20
14) 32

15) 32
16) 56
17) 12
18) 13
19) 53
20) 42

Multiplying and Dividing Integers

1) 16
2) 18
3) 120
4) 72
5) − 132
6) − 50
7) 64

8) 72
9) − 90
10) − 12
11) 6
12) − 6
13) 7
14) 6

15) − 10
16) 6
17) 8
18) − 11
19) 8
20) 4

Ordering Integers and Numbers

1) − 19, − 15, − 4, 1, 20
2) − 5, − 3, 2, 4, 6
3) − 42, − 22, 0, 15, 19
4) − 91, − 55, − 13, 0, 26, 67
5) − 71, − 54, − 39, − 25, − 17, 90

6) 5, 19, 24, 46, 77, 98
7) 6, 5, − 2, − 3, − 4
8) 47, 27, 7, − 17, − 37
9) 32, 19, 15, − 17, − 27
10) 94, 81, 72, 68, 21, − 18

Arrange and Order, Comparing Integers

1) 82, 71, 21, − 10, − 18

2) 20, 15, 12, 11, − 5, − 9

3) 20, 15, 9, − 5, −11

4) 19, 18, − 6, − 9, − 11

5) 56, 32, − 5, − 12, − 34

6) <

7) >

8) >

9) >

10) <

11) >

12) <

13) >

14) =

15) >

Order of Operations

1) 9

2) 15

3) 32

4) 17

5) 33

6) 56

7) 33

8) 49

9) 6

10) − 9

11) 29

12) 9.8

13) 12

14) 62

15) 28

16) 10

17) 50

18) 18

Mixed Integer Computations

1) 14

2) − 42

3) 60

4) − 13

5) − 126

6) 24

7) 3

8) − 3

9) − 2

10) − 9

11) − 16

12) − 4

13) 28

14) − 49

15) 5

16) − 9

17) 12

18) 84

19) − 70

20) − 11

Integers and Absolute Value

1) 4	11) 1	21) 9
2) 7	12) 10	22) 41
3) 8	13) 3	23) 133
4) 4	14) 7	24) 46
5) 5	15) 5	25) 44
6) 10	16) 3	26) 33
7) 1	17) 9	27) 15
8) 6	18) 2	28) 21
9) 8	19) 4	29) 23
10) 2	20) 6	

Chapter 4: Proportions and Ratios

Topics that you'll learn in this chapter:

- ✓ Writing Ratios
- ✓ Simplifying Ratios
- ✓ Create a Proportion
- ✓ Similar Figures
- ✓ Simple Interest
- ✓ Ratio and Rates Word Problems

"Do not worry about your difficulties in mathematics. I can assure you mine are still greater."

– Albert Einstein

Writing Ratios

Helpful	− A ratio is a comparison of two numbers. Ratio can be written as a division.	**Example:**
Hints		$3 : 5$, or $\dfrac{3}{5}$

✎ *Express each ratio as a rate and unite rate.*

1) 120 miles on 4 gallons of gas.

2) 24 dollars for 6 books.

3) 200 miles on 14 gallons of gas

4) 24 inches of snow in 8 hours

✎ *Express each ratio as a fraction in the simplest form.*

5) 3 feet out of 30 feet

6) 18 cakes out of 42 cakes

7) 16 dimes t0 24 dimes

8) 12 dimes out of 48 coins

9) 14 cups to 84 cups

10) 45 gallons to 65 gallons

11) 10 miles out of 40 miles

12) 22 blue cars out of 55 cars

13) 32 pennies to 300 pennies

14) 24 beetles out of 86 insects

Simplifying Ratios

Helpful	— You can calculate equivalent ratios by multiplying or dividing both sides of the ratio by the same number.	**Examples:**
Hints		$3 : 6 = 1 : 2$
		$4 : 9 = 8 : 18$

✎ *Reduce each ratio.*

1) $21 : 49$

2) $20 : 40$

3) $10 : 50$

4) $14 : 18$

5) $45 : 27$

6) $49 : 21$

7) $100 : 10$

8) $12 : 8$

9) $35 : 45$

10) $8 : 20$

11) $25 : 35$

12) $21 : 27$

13) $52 : 82$

14) $12 : 36$

15) $24 : 3$

16) $15 : 30$

17) $3 : 36$

18) $8 : 16$

19) $6 : 100$

20) $2 : 20$

21) $10 : 60$

22) $14 : 63$

23) $68 : 80$

24) $8 : 80$

Create a Proportion

Helpful *Hints*	– A proportion contains 2 equal fractions! A proportion simply means that two fractions are equal. **Example:** 2, 4, 8, 16 $\dfrac{2}{4} = \dfrac{8}{16}$

✐ *Create proportion from the given set of numbers.*

1) 1, 6, 2, 3

2) 12, 144, 1, 12

3) 16, 4, 8, 2

4) 9, 5, 27, 15

5) 7, 10, 60, 42

6) 8, 7, 24, 21

7) 10, 5, 8, 4

8) 3, 12, 8, 2

9) 2, 2, 1, 4

10)   3, 6, 7, 14

11)   2, 6, 5, 15

12)   7, 2, 14, 4

Similar Figures

Helpful **Hints**	– Two or more figures are similar if the corresponding angles are equal, and the corresponding sides are in proportion.	**Example:** 3–4–5 triangle is similar to a 6–8–10 triangle

✍️ *Each pair of figures is similar. Find the missing side.*

1)

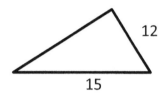 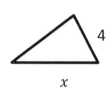

2)

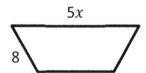 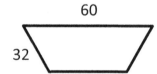

3)

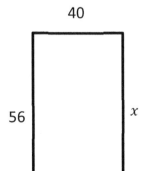 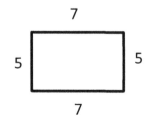

Simple Interest

Helpful	**Simple Interest:** The charge for borrowing money or the return for lending it. Interest = principal x rate x time $$I = prt$$	**Example:** $450 at 7% for 8 years. $$I = prt$$ $$I = 450 \times 0.07 \times 8 = \$252$$
Hints		

✎ *Use simple interest to find the ending balance.*

1) $1,300 at 5% for 6 years.

2) $5,400 at 7.5% for 6 months.

3) $25,600 at 9.2% for 5 years

4) $24,000 at 8.5% for 9 years.

5) $450 at 7% for 8 years.

6) $54,200 at 8% for 5 years.

7) $240 interest is earned on a principal of $1500 at a simple interest rate of 4% interest per year. For how many years was the principal invested?

8) A new car, valued at $28,000, depreciates at 9% per year from original price. Find the value of the car 3 years after purchase.

9) Sara puts $2,000 into an investment yielding 5% annual simple interest; she left the money in for five years. How much interest does Sara get at the end of those five years?

Ratio and Rates Word Problems

Helpful	To solve a ratio or a rate word problem, create a proportion and use cross multiplication method!	**Example:**
Hints		$\dfrac{x}{4} = \dfrac{8}{16}$
		$16x = 4 \times 8$
		$x = 2$

✎ Solve.

1) In a party, 10 soft drinks are required for every 12 guests. If there are 252 guests, how many soft drinks is required?

2) In Jack's class, 18 of the students are tall and 10 are short. In Michael's class 54 students are tall and 30 students are short. Which class has a higher ratio of tall to short students?

3) Are these ratios equivalent?

   12 cards to 72 animals, 11 marbles to 66 marbles

4) The price of 3 apples at the Quick Market is $1.44. The price of 5 of the same apples at Walmart is $2.50. Which place is the better buy?

5) The bakers at a Bakery can make 160 bagels in 4 hours. How many bagels can they bake in 16 hours? What is that rate per hour?

6) You can buy 5 cans of green beans at a supermarket for $3.40. How much does it cost to buy 35 cans of green beans?

Answers of Worksheets – Chapter 4

Writing Ratios

1) $\frac{120\ miles}{4\ gallons}$, 30 miles per gallon

2) $\frac{24\ dollars}{6\ books}$, 4.00 dollars per book

3) $\frac{200\ miles}{14\ gallons}$, 14.29 miles per gallon

4) $\frac{24"\ of\ snow}{8\ hours}$, 3 inches of snow per hour

5) $\frac{1}{10}$

6) $\frac{3}{7}$

7) $\frac{2}{3}$

8) $\frac{1}{4}$

9) $\frac{1}{6}$

10) $\frac{9}{13}$

11) $\frac{1}{4}$

12) $\frac{2}{5}$

13) $\frac{8}{75}$

14) $\frac{12}{43}$

Simplifying Ratios

1) 3 : 7
2) 1 : 2
3) 1 : 5
4) 7 : 9
5) 5 : 3
6) 7 : 3
7) 10 : 1
8) 3 : 2

9) 7 : 9
10) 2 : 5
11) 5 : 7
12) 7 : 9
13) 26 : 41
14) 1 : 3
15) 8 : 1
16) 1 : 2

17) 1 : 12
18) 1 : 2
19) 3 : 50
20) 1 : 10
21) 1: 6
22) 2 : 9
23) 17 : 20
24) 1 : 10

Create a Proportion

1) 1 : 3 = 2 : 6

2) 12 : 144 = 1 : 12

3) 2 : 4 = 8 : 16

4) 5 : 15 = 9 : 27

5) 7 : 42, 10 : 60

6) 7 : 21 = 8 : 24

7) 8 : 10 = 4 : 5

8) 2 : 3 = 8 : 12

9) 4 : 2 = 2 : 1

10) 7 : 3 = 14 : 6   11) 5 : 2 = 15 : 6   12) 7 : 2 = 14 : 4

Similar Figures

1) 5   2) 3   3) 56

Simple Interest

1) $1,690.00   4) $42,360.00   7) 4 years

2) $5,602.50   5) $702.00   8) $20,440

3) $37,376.00   6) $75,880.00   9) $500

Ratio and Rates Word Problems

1) 210

2) The ratio for both class is equal to 9 to 5.

3) Yes! Both ratios are 1 to 6

4) The price at the Quick Market is a better buy.

5) 640, the rate is 40 per hour.

6) $23.80

Chapter 5: Percent

Topics that you'll learn in this chapter:

- ✓ Percentage Calculations
- ✓ Converting Between Percent, Fractions, and Decimals
- ✓ Percent Problems
- ✓ Markup, Discount, and Tax

"The book of nature is written in the language of Mathematic" -Galileo

Percentage Calculations

Helpful Hints	- Use the following formula to find part, whole, or percent: $$part = \frac{percent}{100} \times whole$$	Example: $$\frac{20}{100} \times 100 = 20$$

✎ **Calculate the percentages.**

1) 50% of 25

2) 80% of 15

3) 30% of 34

4) 70% of 45

5) 10% of 0

6) 80% of 22

7) 65% of 8

8) 78% of 54

9) 50% of 80

10) 20% of 10

11) 40% of 40

12) 90% of 0

13) 20% of 70

14) 55% of 60

15) 80% of 10

16) 20% of 880

17) 70% of 100

18) 80% of 90

✎ **Solve.**

19) 50 is what percentage of 75?

20) What percentage of 100 is 70

21) Find what percentage of 60 is 35.

22) 40 is what percentage of 80?

Converting Between Percent, Fractions, and Decimals

Helpful	– To a percent: Move the decimal point 2 places to the right and add the % symbol.	**Examples:**
Hints	– Divide by 100 to convert a number from percent to decimal.	30% = 0.3
		0.24 = 24%

✍ *Converting fractions to decimals.*

1) $\dfrac{50}{100}$ 4) $\dfrac{80}{100}$ 7) $\dfrac{90}{100}$

2) $\dfrac{38}{100}$ 5) $\dfrac{7}{100}$ 8) $\dfrac{20}{100}$

3) $\dfrac{15}{100}$ 6) $\dfrac{35}{100}$ 9) $\dfrac{7}{100}$

✍ *Write each decimal as a percent.*

10) 0.5   13) 0.524   16) 3.63

11) 0.9   14) 0.1   17) 0.008

12) 0.002   15) 0.03   18) 4.78

Percent Problems

Helpful	Base = Part ÷ Percent	**Example:**
	Part = Percent × Base	2 is 10% of 20.
Hints	Percent = Part ÷ Base	2 ÷ 0.10 = 20
		2 = 0.10 × 20
		0.10 = 2 ÷ 20

✍ **Solve each problem.**

1) 51 is 340% of what?

2) 93% of what number is 97?

3) 27% of 142 is what number?

4) What percent of 125 is 29.3?

5) 60 is what percent of 126?

6) 67 is 67% of what?

7) 67 is 13% of what?

8) 41% of 78 is what?

9) 1 is what percent of 52.6?

10) What is 59% of 14 m?

11) What is 90% of 130 inches?

12) 16 inches is 35% of what?

13) 90% of 54.4 hours is what?

14) What percent of 33.5 is 21?

15) Liam scored 22 out of 30 marks in Algebra, 35 out of 40 marks in science and 89 out of 100 marks in mathematics. In which subject his percentage of marks in best?

16) Ella require 50% to pass. If she gets 280 marks and falls short by 20 marks, what were the maximum marks she could have got?

Markup, Discount, and Tax

Helpful

Hints

- **Markup** = selling price − cost
  Markup rate = markup divided by the cost

- **Discount:**
  Multiply the regular price by the rate of discount

  Selling price =

  original price − discount

- **Tax:**
  To find tax, multiply the tax rate to the taxable amount (income, property value, etc.)

Example:

Original price of a microphone: $49.99, discount: 5%, tax: 5%

Selling price = 49.87

✎ *Find the selling price of each item.*

1) Cost of a pen: $1.95, markup: 70%, discount: 40%, tax: 5%

2) Cost of a puppy: $349.99, markup: 41%, discount: 23%

3) Cost of a shirt: $14.95, markup: 25%, discount: 45%

4) Cost of an oil change: $21.95, markup: 95%

5) Cost of computer: $1,850.00, markup: 75%

Answers of Worksheets – Chapter 5

Percentage Calculations

1) 12.5	9) 40	17) 70
2) 12	10) 2	18) 72
3) 10.2	11) 16	19) 67%
4) 31.5	12) 0	20) 70%
5) 0	13) 14	21) 58%
6) 17.6	14) 33	22) 50%
7) 5.2	15) 8	
8) 42.12	16) 176	

Converting Between Percent, Fractions, and Decimals

1) 0.5	7) 0.9	13) 52.4%
2) 0.38	8) 0.2	14) 10%
3) 0.15	9) 0.07	15) 3%
4) 0.8	10) 50%	16) 363%
5) 0.07	11) 90%	17) 0.8%
6) 0.35	12) 0.2%	18) 478%

Percent Problems

1) 15	7) 515.4	13) 49 hours
2) 104.3	8) 31.98	14) 62.7%
3) 38.34	9) 1.9%	15) Mathematics
4) 23.44%	10) 8.3 m	16) 600
5) 47.6%	11) 117 inches	
6) 100	12) 45.7 inches	

Markup, Discount, and Tax

1) $2.09

2) $379.98

3) $10.28

4) $36.22

5) $3,237.50

Chapter 6: Algebraic Expressions

Topics that you'll learn in this chapter:

- ✓ Expressions and Variables
- ✓ Simplifying Variable Expressions
- ✓ Simplifying Polynomial Expressions
- ✓ Translate Phrases into an Algebraic Statement
- ✓ The Distributive Property
- ✓ Evaluating One Variable
- ✓ Evaluating Two Variables
- ✓ Combining like Terms

Without mathematics, there's nothing you can do. Everything around you is mathematics.
Everything around you is numbers." – Shakuntala Devi

Expressions and Variables

Helpful	A variable is a letter that represents unknown numbers. A variable can be used in the same manner as all other numbers:		
Hints			
	Addition	2 + a	2 plus a
	Subtraction	$y - 3$	y minus 3
	Division	$\dfrac{4}{x}$	4 divided by x
	Multiplication	5a	5 times a

✎ *Simplify each expression.*

1) $x + 5x$,

   use $x = 5$

2) $8(-3x + 9) + 6$,

   use $x = 6$

3) $10x - 2x + 6 - 5$,

   use $x = 5$

4) $2x - 3x - 9$,

   use $x = 7$

5) $(-6)(-2x - 4y)$,

   use $x = 1, y = 3$

6) $8x + 2 + 4y$,

   use $x = 9, y = 2$

7) $(-6)(-8x - 9y)$,

   use $x = 5, y = 5$

8) $6x + 5y$,

   use $x = 7, y = 4$

✎ *Simplify each expression.*

9) $5(-4 + 2x)$

10) $-3 - 5x - 6x + 9$

11) $6x - 3x - 8 + 10$

12) $(-8)(6x - 4) + 12$

13) $9(7x + 4) + 6x$

14) $(-9)(-5x + 2)$

Simplifying Variable Expressions

Helpful	− Combine "like" terms. (values with same variable and same power)	**Example:**
	− Use distributive property if necessary.	$2x + 2\,(1 - 5x) =$
Hints		$2x + 2 - 10x = -8x + 2$
	Distributive Property:	
	$a\,(b\,+\,c)\,=\,ab\,+\,ac$	

✍ *Simplify each expression.*

1) $-2 - x^2 - 6x^2$

2) $3 + 10x^2 + 2$

3) $8x^2 + 6x + 7x^2$

4) $5x^2 - 12x^2 + 8x$

5) $2x^2 - 2x - x$

6) $(-6)\,(8x - 4)$

7) $4x + 6\,(2 - 5x)$

8) $10x + 8\,(10x - 6)$

9) $9\,(-2x - 6) - 5$

10) $3\,(x + 9)$

11) $7x + 3 - 3x$

12) $2.5x^2 \times (-8x)$

✍ *Simplify.*

13) $-2(4 - 6x) - 3x,\ x = 1$

14) $2x + 8x,\ x = 2$

15) $9 - 2x + 5x + 2,\ x = 5$

16) $5\,(3x + 7),\ x = 3$

17) $2\,(3 - 2x) - 4,\ x = 6$

18) $5x + 3x - 8,\ x = 3$

19) $x - 7x,\ x = 8$

20) $5\,(-2 - 9x),\ x = 4$

Simplifying Polynomial Expressions

Helpful	-	In mathematics, a polynomial is an expression consisting of variables and coefficients that involves only the operations of addition, subtraction, multiplication, and non–negative integer exponents of variables.	**Example:**

Helpful

Hints

In mathematics, a polynomial is an expression consisting of variables and coefficients that involves only the operations of addition, subtraction, multiplication, and non–negative integer exponents of variables.

$$P(x) = a_0x^n + a_1x^{n-1} + \dots + a_{n-2}2x^2 + a_{n-1}x + a_n$$

Example:

An example of a polynomial of a single indeterminate x is

$x^2 - 4x + 7$.

An example for three variables is

$x^3 + 2xyz^2 - yz + 1$

✎ *Simplify each polynomial.*

1) $4x^5 - 5x^6 + 15x^5 - 12x^6 + 3\ x^6$

2) $(-3x^5 + 12 - 4x) + (8x^4 + 5x + 5\ x^5)$

3) $10x^2 - 5x^4 + 14x^3 - 20x^4 + 15x^3 - 8x^4$

4) $-6x^2 + 5x^2 - 7x^3 + 12 + 22$

5) $12x^5 - 5x^3 + 8x^2 - 8x^5$

6) $5x^3 + 1 + x^2 - 2x - 10x$

7) $14x^2 - 6x^3 - 2x\ (4x^2 + 2x)$

8) $(4x^4 - 2x) - (4x - 2x^4)$

9) $(3x^2 + 1) - (4 + 2x^2)$

10) $(2x + 2) - (7x + 6)$

11) $(12x^3 + 4x^4) - (2x^4 - 6x^3)$

12) $(12 + 3x^3) + (6x^3 + 6)$

13) $(5x^2 - 3) + (2x^2 - 3x^3)$

14) $(23x^3 - 12x^2) - (2x^2 - 9x^3)$

15) $(4x - 3x^3) - (3x^3 + 4x)$

Translate Phrases into an Algebraic Statement

Helpful

Hints

Translating key words and phrases into algebraic expressions:

Addition: plus, more than, the sum of, etc.

Subtraction: minus, less than, decreased, etc.

Multiplication: times, product, multiplied, etc.

Division: quotient, divided, ratio, etc.

Example:

eight more than a number is 20

$8 + x = 20$

✍ *Write an algebraic expression for each phrase.*

1) A number increased by forty–two.

2) The sum of fifteen and a number

3) The difference between fifty–six and a number.

4) The quotient of thirty and a number.

5) Twice a number decreased by 25.

6) Four times the sum of a number and − 12.

7) A number divided by − 20.

8) The quotient of 60 and the product of a number and − 5.

9) Ten subtracted from a number.

10) The difference of six and a number.

The Distributive Property

Helpful Hints	Distributive Property: $a\,(b\,+\,c)\,=\,ab\,+\,ac$	Example: $3\,(4\,+\,3x)$ $=\,12\,+\,9x$

✎ *Use the distributive property to simply each expression.*

1) $-(-2-5x)$

2) $(-6x+2)(-1)$

3) $(-5)\,(x-2)$

4) $-(7-3x)$

5) $8\,(8+2x)$

6) $2\,(12+2x)$

7) $(-6x+8)\,4$

8) $(3-6x)(-7)$

9) $(-12)\,(2x+1)$

10) $(8-2x)\,9$

11) $(-2x)\,(-1+9x)-4x\,(4+5x)$

12) $3\,(-5x-3)+4(6-3x)$

13) $(-2)(x+4)-(2+3x)$

14) $(-4)(3x-2)+6\,(x+1)$

15) $(-5)(4x-1)+4\,(x+2)$

16) $(-3)(x+4)-(2+3x)$

Evaluating One Variable

Helpful	– To evaluate one variable expression, find the variable and substitute a number for that variable.	**Example:**
Hints	– Perform the arithmetic operations.	$4x + 8, x = 6$ $4(6) + 8 = 24 + 8 = 32$

✍ *Simplify each algebraic expression.*

1) $9 - x$, $x = 3$

2) $x + 2$, $x = 5$

3) $3x + 7$, $x = 6$

4) $x + (-5)$, $x = -2$

5) $3x + 6$, $x = 4$

6) $4x + 6$, $x = -1$

7) $10 + 2x - 6$, $x = 3$

8) $10 - 3x$, $x = 8$

9) $\dfrac{20}{x} - 3$, $x = 5$

10) $(-3) + \dfrac{x}{4} + 2x$, $x = 16$

11) $(-2) + \dfrac{x}{7}$, $x = 21$

12) $(-\dfrac{14}{x}) - 9 + 4x$, $x = 2$

13) $(-\dfrac{6}{x}) - 9 + 2x$, $x = 3$

14) $(-2) + \dfrac{x}{8}$, $x = 16$

Evaluating Two Variables

Helpful	To evaluate an algebraic expression, substitute a number for each variable and perform the arithmetic operations.	**Example:**
Hints		$2x + 4y - 3 + 2,$
		$x = 5, y = 3$
		$2(5) + 4(3) - 3 + 2$
		$= 10$
		$+ 12 - 3 + 2$
		$= 21$

✎ *Simplify each algebraic expression.*

1) $2x + 4y - 3 + 2,$

   $x = 5, y = 3$

2) $(-\frac{12}{x}) + 1 + 5y,$

   $x = 6, y = 8$

3) $(-4)(-2a - 2b),$

   $a = 5, b = 3$

4) $10 + 3x + 7 - 2y,$

   $x = 7, y = 6$

5) $9x + 2 - 4y,$

   $x = 7, y = 5$

6) $6 + 3(-2x - 3y),$

   $x = 9, y = 7$

7) $12x + y,$

   $x = 4, y = 8$

8) $x \times 4 \div y,$

   $x = 3, y = 2$

9) $2x + 14 + 4y,$

   $x = 6, y = 8$

10) $4a - (5 - b),$

    $a = 4, b = 6$

Combining like Terms

Helpful *Hints*	– Terms are separated by "+" and "–" signs. – Like terms are terms with same variables and same powers. – Be sure to use the "+" or "–" that is in front of the coefficient.	**Example:** $22x + 6 + 2x =$ $24x + 6$

✍ *Simplify each expression.*

1) $5 + 2x - 8$

2) $(-2x + 6)\,2$

3) $7 + 3x + 6x - 4$

4) $(-4) - (3)(5x + 8)$

5) $9x - 7x - 5$

6) $x - 12x$

7) $7(3x + 6) + 2x$

8) $(-11x) - 10x$

9) $3x - 12 - 5x$

10) $13 + 4x - 5$

11) $(-22x) + 8x$

12) $2(4 + 3x) - 7x$

13) $(-4x) - (6 - 14x)$

14) $5(6x - 1) + 12x$

15) $22x + 6 + 2x$

16) $(-13x) - 14x$

17) $(-6x) - 9 + 15x$

18) $(-6x) + 7x$

19) $(-5x) + 12 + 7x$

20) $(-3x) - 9 + 15x$

21) $20x - 19x$

Answers of Worksheets – Chapter 6

Expressions and Variables

1) 30
2) −66
3) 41
4) −16
5) 84
6) 82
7) 510
8) 62
9) $10x − 20$
10) $6 − 11x$
11) $3x + 2$
12) $44 − 48x$
13) $69x + 36$
14) $45x − 18$

Simplifying Variable Expressions

1) $− 7x^2 − 2$
2) $10x^2 + 5$
3) $15x^2 + 6x$
4) $− 7x^2 + 8x$
5) $2x^2 − 3x$
6) $− 48x + 24$
7) $− 26x + 12$
8) $90x − 48$
9) $− 18x − 59$
10) $3x + 27$
11) $4x + 3$
12) $− 20x^3$
13) 1
14) 20
15) 26
16) 80
17) $− 22$
18) 16
19) $− 48$
20) $− 190$

Simplifying Polynomial Expressions

1) $− 14x^6 + 19x^5$
2) $2x^5 + 8x^4 + x + 12$
3) $−33x^4 + 29x^3 + 10x^2$
4) $−7x^3 − x^2 + 34$
5) $4x^5 − 5x^3 + 8x^2$
6) $5x^3 + x^2 − 12x + 1$
7) $−14x^3 + 10x^2$
8) $6x^4 − 6x$
9) $x^2 − 3$
10) $− 5x − 4$
11) $2x^4 + 18x^3$
12) $9x^3 + 18$
13) $−3x^3 + 7x^2 − 3$
14) $32x^3 − 14x^2$
15) $−6x^3$

Translate Phrases into an Algebraic Statement

1) $x + 42$
3) $56 − x$
4) $30/x$
5) $2x − 25$
8) $\dfrac{60}{−5x}$
2) $15 + x$
6) $4(x + (−12))$
7) $\dfrac{x}{−20}$
9) $x − 10$
10) $6 − x$

The Distributive Property

1) $5x + 2$

2) $6x - 2$

3) $-5x + 10$

4) $3x - 7$

5) $16x + 64$

6) $4x + 24$

7) $-24x + 32$

8) $42x - 21$

9) $-24x - 12$

10) $-18x + 72$

11) $-38x^2 - 14x$

12) $-27x + 15$

13) $-5x - 10$

14) $-6x + 14$

15) $-16x + 13$

16) $-6x - 14$

Evaluating One Variable

1) 6

2) 7

3) 25

4) −7

5) 18

6) 2

7) 10

8) −14

9) 1

10) 33

11) 1

12) −8

13) −5

14) 0

Evaluating Two Variables

1) 21

2) 39

3) 64

4) 26

5) 45

6) −111

7) 56

8) 6

9) 58

10) 17

Combining like Terms

1) $2x - 3$

2) $-4x + 12$

3) $9x + 3$

4) $-15x - 28$

5) $2x - 5$

6) $-11x$

7) $23x + 42$

8) $-21x$

9) $-2x - 12$

10) $4x + 8$

11) $-14x$

12) $-x + 8$

13) $10x - 6$

14) $42x - 5$

15) $24x + 6$

16) $-27x$

17) $9x - 9$

18) x

19) $2x + 12$

20) $12x - 9$

21) x

Chapter 7: Equations

Topics that you'll learn in this chapter:

- ✓ One– Step Equations
- ✓ Two– Step Equations
- ✓ Multi– Step Equations

"The study of mathematics, like the Nile, begins in minuteness but ends in magnificence."

– Charles Caleb Colton

One–Step Equations

| Helpful | - | The values of two expressions on both sides of an equation are equal. $$ax + b = c$$ | Example: $$-8x = 16$$ |
| Hints | - | You only need to perform one Math operation in order to solve the equation. | $$x = -2$$ |

✏ *Solve each equation.*

1) $x + 3 = 17$

2) $22 = (-8) + x$

3) $3x = (-30)$

4) $(-36) = (-6x)$

5) $(-6) = 4 + x$

6) $2 + x = (-2)$

7) $20x = (-220)$

8) $18 = x + 5$

9) $(-23) + x = (-19)$

10) $5x = (-45)$

11) $x - 12 = (-25)$

12) $x - 3 = (-12)$

13) $(-35) = x - 27$

14) $8 = 2x$

15) $(-6x) = 36$

16) $(-55) = (-5x)$

17) $x - 30 = 20$

18) $8x = 32$

19) $36 = (-4x)$

20) $4x = 68$

21) $30x = 300$

Two–Step Equations

Helpful	– You only need to perform two math operations (add, subtract, multiply, or divide) to solve the equation.	Example:
Hints	– Simplify using the inverse of addition or subtraction.	$-2(x-1) = 42$ $(x-1) = -21$
	– Simplify further by using the inverse of multiplication or division.	$x = -20$

✎ *Solve each equation.*

1) $5(8+x) = 20$

2) $(-7)(x-9) = 42$

3) $(-12)(2x-3) = (-12)$

4) $6(1+x) = 12$

5) $12(2x+4) = 60$

6) $7(3x+2) = 42$

7) $8(14+2x) = (-34)$

8) $(-15)(2x-4) = 48$

9) $3(x+5) = 12$

10) $\dfrac{3x-12}{6} = 4$

11) $(-12) = \dfrac{x+15}{6}$

12) $110 = (-5)(2x-6)$

13) $\dfrac{x}{8} - 12 = 4$

14) $20 = 12 + \dfrac{x}{4}$

15) $\dfrac{-24+x}{6} = (-12)$

16) $(-4)(5+2x) = (-100)$

17) $(-12x) + 20 = 32$

18) $\dfrac{-2+6x}{4} = (-8)$

19) $\dfrac{x+6}{5} = (-5)$

20) $(-9) + \dfrac{x}{4} = (-15)$

Multi–Step Equations

Helpful *Hints*	– Combine "like" terms on one side. – Bring variables to one side by adding or subtracting. – Simplify using the inverse of addition or subtraction. – Simplify further by using the inverse of multiplication or division.	**Example:** $3x + 15 = -2x + 5$ Add 2x both sides $5x + 15 = +5$ Subtract 15 both sides $5x = -10$ Divide by 5 both sides $x = -2$

✎*Solve each equation.*

1) $-(2 - 2x) = 10$

2) $-12 = -(2x + 8)$

3) $3x + 15 = (-2x) + 5$

4) $-28 = (-2x) - 12x$

5) $2(1 + 2x) + 2x = -118$

6) $3x - 18 = 22 + x - 3 + x$

7) $12 - 2x = (-32) - x + x$

8) $7 - 3x - 3x = 3 - 3x$

9) $6 + 10x + 3x = (-30) + 4x$

10) $(-3x) - 8(-1 + 5x) = 352$

11) $24 = (-4x) - 8 + 8$

12) $9 = 2x - 7 + 6x$

13) $6(1 + 6x) = 294$

14) $-10 = (-4x) - 6x$

15) $4x - 2 = (-7) + 5x$

16) $5x - 14 = 8x + 4$

17) $40 = -(4x - 8)$

18) $(-18) - 6x = 6(1 + 3x)$

19) $x - 5 = -2(6 + 3x)$

20) $6 = 1 - 2x + 5$

Answers of Worksheets – Chapter 7

One–Step Equations

1) 14	8) 13	15) − 6
2) 30	9) 4	16) 11
3) − 10	10) − 9	17) 50
4) 6	11) − 13	18) 4
5) − 10	12) − 9	19) − 9
6) − 4	13) − 8	20) 17
7) − 11	14) 4	21) 10

Two–Step Equations

1) − 4	8) $\frac{2}{5}$	15) − 48
2) 3	9) − 1	16) 10
3) 2	10) 12	17) − 1
4) 1	11) − 87	18) − 5
5) 0.5	12) − 8	19) − 31
6) $\frac{4}{3}$	13) 128	20) − 24
7) $-\frac{73}{8}$	14) 32	

Multi–Step Equations

1) 6	8) $\frac{4}{3}$	14) 1
2) 2	9) − 4	15) 5
3) − 2	10) − 8	16) − 6
4) 2	11) − 6	17) − 8
5) − 20	12) 2	18) − 1
6) 37	13) 8	19) − 1
7) 22		20) 0

Chapter 8: Inequalities

Topics that you'll learn in this chapter:

- ✓ Graphing Single– Variable Inequalities
- ✓ One– Step Inequalities
- ✓ Two– Step Inequalities
- ✓ Multi– Step Inequalities

Without mathematics, there's nothing you can do. Everything around you is mathematics. Everything around you is numbers." – Shakuntala Devi

Graphing Single–Variable Inequalities

Helpful *Hints*	– Isolate the variable.
	– Find the value of the inequality on the number line.
	– For less than or greater than draw open circle on the value of the variable.
	– If there is an equal sign too, then use filled circle.
	– Draw a line to the right direction.

✎*Draw a graph for each inequality.*

1) $-2 > x$

2) $5 \leq -x$

3) $x > 7$

4) $-x > 1.5$

One–Step Inequalities

Helpful *Hints*	– Isolate the variable. – For dividing both sides by negative numbers, flip the direction of the inequality sign.	**Example:** $x + 4 \geq 11$ $x \geq 7$

✎ *Solve each inequality and graph it.*

1) $x + 9 \geq 11$

2) $x - 4 \leq 2$

3) $6x \geq 36$

4) $7 + x < 16$

5) $x + 8 \leq 1$

6) $3x > 12$

7) $3x < 24$

Two–Step Inequalities

		Example:
Helpful	– Isolate the variable.	
	– For dividing both sides by negative numbers, flip the direction of the of the inequality sign.	$2x + 9 \geq 11$
Hints		$2x \geq 2$
	– Simplify using the inverse of addition or subtraction.	$x \geq 1$
	– Simplify further by using the inverse of multiplication or division.	

✎ *Solve each inequality and graph it.*

1) $3x - 4 \leq 5$

2) $2x - 2 \leq 6$

3) $4x - 4 \leq 8$

4) $3x + 6 \geq 12$

5) $6x - 5 \geq 19$

6) $2x - 4 \leq 6$

7) $8x - 4 \leq 4$

8) $6x + 4 \leq 10$

9) $5x + 4 \leq 9$

10) $7x - 4 \leq 3$

11) $4x - 19 < 19$

12) $2x - 3 < 21$

13) $7 + 4x \geq 19$

14) $9 + 4x < 21$

15) $3 + 2x \geq 19$

16) $6 + 4x < 22$

Multi–Step Inequalities

Helpful Hints	– Isolate the variable.	Example:
	– Simplify using the inverse of addition or subtraction.	$\dfrac{7x + 1}{3} \geq 5$
	– Simplify further by using the inverse of multiplication or division.	$7x + 1 \geq 15$
		$7x \geq 14$
		$x \geq 7$

✎ *Solve each inequality.*

1) $\dfrac{9x}{7} - 7 < 2$

2) $\dfrac{4x + 8}{2} \leq 12$

3) $\dfrac{3x - 8}{7} > 1$

4) $-3(x - 7) > 21$

5) $4 + \dfrac{x}{3} < 7$

6) $\dfrac{2x + 6}{4} \leq 10$

Answers of Worksheets – Chapter 8

Graphing Single–Variable Inequalities

1) $-2 > x$

2) $x \leq -5$

3) $x > 7$

4) $-1.5 > x$

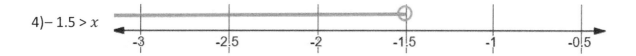

One–Step Inequalities

1)

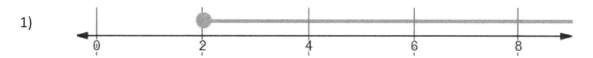

2)

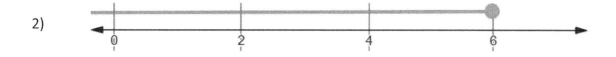

3)

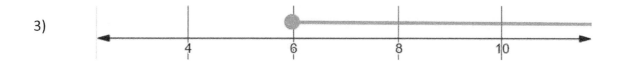

4)

5)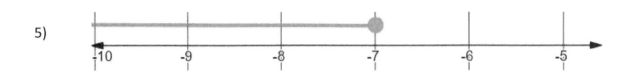

6)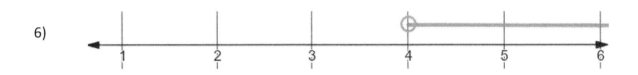

7)

Two–Step inequalities

1) $x \leq 3$

2) $x \leq 4$

3) $x \leq 3$

4) $x \geq 2$

5) $x \geq 4$

6) $x \leq 5$

7) $x \leq 1$

8) $x \leq 1$

9) $x \leq 1$

10) $x \leq 1$

11) $x < 9.5$

12) $x < 12$

13) $x \geq 3$

14) $x < 3$

15) $x \geq 8$

16) $x < 4$

Multi–Step inequalities

1) $x < 7$

2) $x \leq 4$

3) $x > 5$

4) $x < 0$

5) $x < 9$

6) $x \leq 17$

Chapter 9: Linear Functions

Topics that you'll learn in this chapter:

- ✓ Finding Slope
- ✓ Graphing Lines Using Slope– Intercept Form
- ✓ Graphing Lines Using Standard Form
- ✓ Writing Linear Equations
- ✓ Graphing Linear Inequalities
- ✓ Finding Midpoint
- ✓ Finding Distance of Two Points
- ✓ Slope–intercept form
- ✓ Equations of horizontal and vertical lines
- ✓ Equation of parallel or perpendicular lines

"Sometimes the questions are complicated, and the answers are simple." – Dr. Seuss

Finding Slope

Helpful	**Slope of a line:**	**Example:**
Hints	$$\frac{y_2 - y_1}{x_2 - x_1} = \frac{rise}{run}$$	$(2, -10), (3, 6)$ slope = 16

✎*Find the slope of the line through each pair of points.*

1) $(1, 1), (3, 5)$

2) $(4, -6), (-3, -8)$

3) $(7, -12), (5, 10)$

4) $(19, 3), (20, 3)$

5) $(15, 8), (-17, 9)$

6) $(6, -12), (15, -3)$

7) $(3, 1), (7, -5)$

8) $(3, -2), (-7, 8)$

9) $(15, -3), (-9, 5)$

10) $(-4, 7), (-6, -4)$

11) $(6, -8), (-11, -7)$

12) $(-6, 13), (17, -9)$

13) $(-10, -2), (-6, -5)$

14) $(4, 5), (-4, 10)$

15) $(-3, 1), (-17, 2)$

16) $(7, 0), (-13, -11)$

17) $(17, -13), (17, 8)$

18) $(12, 2), (-7, 5)$

Graphing Lines Using Slope–Intercept Form

Helpful	**Slope–intercept form:** given the slope *m* and the y–intercept *b*, then the equation of the line is:
Hints	$y = mx + b.$

Example:

$y = 8x - 3$

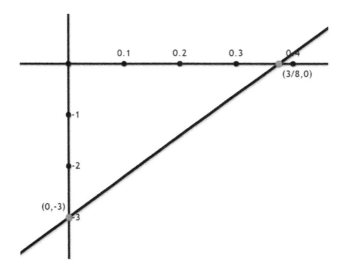

✍ **Sketch the graph of each line.**

1) $y = \frac{1}{2}x - 4$

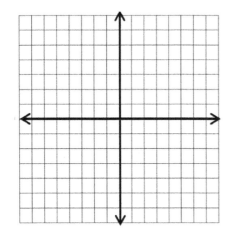

2) $y = 2x$

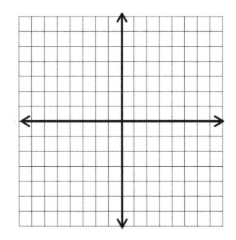

Graphing Lines Using Standard Form

Example:

$x + 4y = 12$

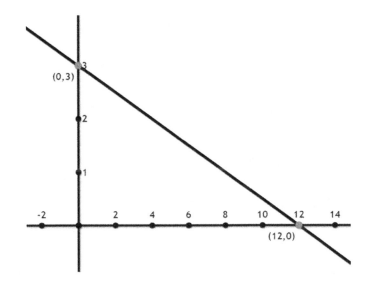

$\nearrow$ **Sketch the graph of each line.**

1) $2x - y = 4$

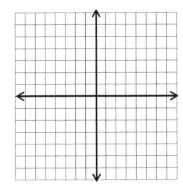

2) $x + y = 2$

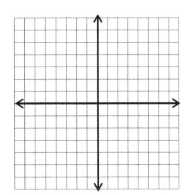

Writing Linear Equations

Helpful	The equation of a line:	Example:
	$$y = mx + b$$	through:
Hints	1– Identify the slope.	$(-4, -2), (-3, 5)$
	2– Find the y–intercept. This can be done by substituting the slope and the coordinates of a point (x, y) on the line.	$$y = 7x + 26$$

✍ *Write the slope–intercept form of the equation of the line through the given points.*

1) through: $(-4, -2), (-3, 5)$

2) through: $(5, 4), (-4, 3)$

3) through: $(0, -2), (-5, 3)$

4) through: $(-1, 1), (-2, 6)$

5) through: $(0, 3), (-4, -1)$

6) through: $(0, 2), (1, -3)$

7) through: $(0, -5), (4, 3)$

8) through: $(-1, 4), (0, 4)$

9) through: $(2, -3), (3, -5)$

10) through: $(2, 5), (-1, -4)$

11) through: $(1, -3), (-3, 1)$

12) through: $(3, 3), (1, -5)$

13) through: $(4, 4), (3, -5)$

14) through: $(0, 3), (1, 1)$

15) through: $(5, 5), (2, -3)$

16) through: $(-2, -2), (2, -5)$

17) through: $(-3, -2), (1, -1)$

18) through: $(-2, 1), (6, 5)$

Graphing Linear Inequalities

Helpful	1– First, graph the "equals" line.
	2– Choose a testing point. (it can be any point on both sides of the line.)
Hints	3– Put the value of (x, y) of that point in the inequality. If that works, that part of the line is the solution. If the values don't work, then the other part of the line is the solution.

✑*Sketch the graph of each linear inequality.*

1) $y < - 4x + 2$

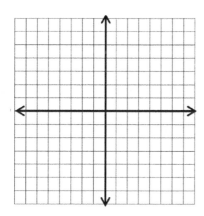

2) $2x + y < - 4$

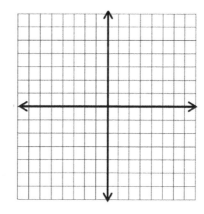

4) $x - 3y < - 5$

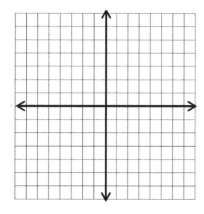

5) $6x - 2y \geq 8$

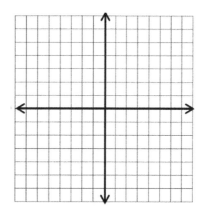

Finding Midpoint

Helpful	Midpoint of the segment AB:	Example:
Hints	$M\left(\dfrac{x_1+x_2}{2}, \dfrac{y_1+y_2}{2}\right)$	$(3, 9), (-1, 6)$ $M\ (1, 7.5)$

🖎 *Find the midpoint of the line segment with the given endpoints.*

1) $(2, -2), (3, -5)$

2) $(0, 2), (-2, -6)$

3) $(7, 4), (9, -1)$

4) $(4, -5), (0, 8)$

5) $(1, -2), (1, -6)$

6) $(-2, -3), (3, -6)$

7) $(7, 0), (-7, 5)$

8) $(-2, 6), (-3, -2)$

9) $(-1, 1), (5, -5)$

10) $(2.3, -1.3), (-2.2, -0.5)$

11) $(4.1, 6.32), (4, 5.6)$

12) $(2, -1), (-6, 0)$

13) $(-4, 4), (5, -1)$

14) $(-2, -3), (-6, 5)$

15) $\left(\dfrac{1}{2}, 1\right), (2, 4)$

16) $(-2, -2), (6, 5)$

Finding Distance of Two Points

Helpful	Distance from A to B:	**Example:**
	$$d = \sqrt{(x_1 - x_2)^2 + (y_1 - y_2)^2}$$	$(-1, 2), (-1, -7)$
Hints		Distance = 9

✍ *Find the distance between each pair of points.*

1) $(2, -1), (1, -1)$

2) $(6, 4), (-1, 3)$

3) $(-8, -5), (-6, 1)$

4) $(-6, -10), (-2, -10)$

5) $(4, -6), (-3, 4)$

6) $(-6, -7), (-2, -8)$

7) $(5, 4), (8, 2)$

8) $(8, 4), (3, -7)$

9) $(1, 3), (5, 7)$

10) $(4, 2), (-7, 1)$

11) $(-3, -4), (-7, -2)$

12) $(-7, -2), (6, 9)$

13) $(10, 0), (0, 4)$

14) $(-3, 2), (5, 0)$

15) $(-5, 6), (8, -4)$

16) $(3, -5), (-8, -4)$

17) $(0, 8), (4, 10)$

18) $(6, 4), (-5, -1)$

Slope–intercept Form

Helpful	Using the slope m and the	Example:
Hints	y-intercept b, then the equation of the line is:	
	$$y = mx + b$$	$y = -10 + 2x$
		$m = 2$

✎ *Write the slope–intercept form of the equation of each line.*

1) $-14x + y = 7$

2) $-2(2x + y) = 28$

3) $-11x - 7y = -56$

4) $9x + 35 = -5y$

5) $x - 3y = 6$

6) $13x - 11y = -12$

7) $11x - 8y = -48$

8) $3x - 2y = -16$

9) $2y = -6x - 8$

10) $2y = -4x + 10$

11) $2y = -2x - 4$

12) $6x + 5y = -15$

Equations of Horizontal and Vertical Lines

Helpful	The slope of horizontal lines is 0. Thus, the equation of horizontal lines becomes: $y = b$
Hints	The slope of vertical lines is undefined and the equation for a vertical line is: $x = a$

✎*Sketch the graph of each line.*

1) $y = 0$

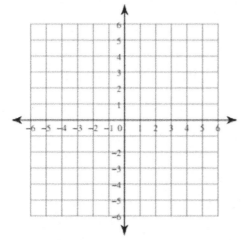

2) $y = 2$

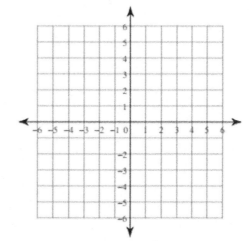

3) $x = -4$

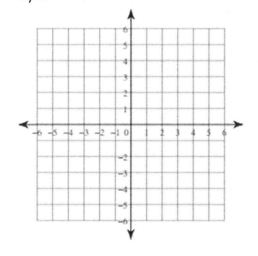

4) $x = 3$

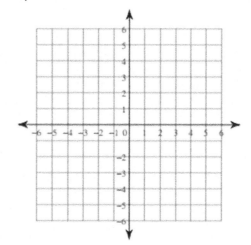

Equation of Parallel or Perpendicular Lines

Helpful

Hints

Parallel lines: are distinct lines with the same slope. For example: if the following lines are parallel:

$y = m_1x + b_1$

$y = m_2x + b_2$

Then, $m_1 = m_2$ and $b_1 \neq b_2$.

Perpendicular Lines: A pair of lines is perpendicular if the lines meet at 90° angle.

$y = m_1x + b_1$

$y = m_2x + b_2$

The two lines are perpendicular if, $m_1 = -\frac{1}{m_2}$, that is, if the slopes are negative reciprocals of each other.

✎ *Write an equation of the line that passes through the given point and is parallel to the given line.*

1) $(-2, -4), 4x + 7y = -14$

2) $(-4, 2), y = -x + 3$

3) $(-2, 5), 2y = 4x - 6$

4) $(-10, 0), -y + 3x = 16$

5) $(5, -1), y = -\frac{3}{5}x - 3$

6) $(1, 7), -6x + y = -1$

7) $(2, -3), y = \frac{1}{5}x + 5$

8) $(1, 4), -6x + 5y = -10$

9) $(3, -3), y = -\frac{5}{2}x - 1$

10) $(-4, 3), 2x + 3y = -9$

✎ *Write an equation of the line that passes through the given point and is perpendicular to the given line.*

11) $(-1, -7), 3x + 12y = -6$

12) $(-3, 5), 5x - 6y = 9$

13) $(2, 6), y = -3$

14) $(-2, 3), x = 4$

15) $(1, -5), y = \frac{1}{8}x + 2$

16) $(3, 4), y = -2x - 4$

17) $(-5, 5), y = \frac{5}{9}x - 4$

18) $(4, -1), y = x + 2$

Answers of Worksheets – Chapter 9

Finding Slope

1) 2

2) $\frac{2}{7}$

3) −11

4) 0

5) $-\frac{1}{32}$

6) 1

7) $-\frac{3}{2}$

8) −1

9) $-\frac{1}{3}$

10) $\frac{11}{2}$

11) $-\frac{1}{17}$

12) $-\frac{22}{23}$

13) $-\frac{3}{4}$

14) $-\frac{5}{8}$

15) $-\frac{1}{14}$

16) $\frac{11}{20}$

17) Undefined

18) $-\frac{3}{19}$

Graphing Lines Using Slope–Intercept Form

1)

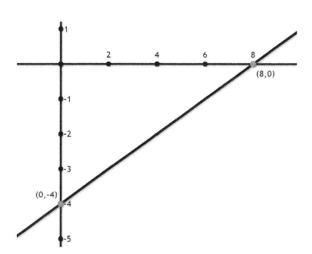

2)

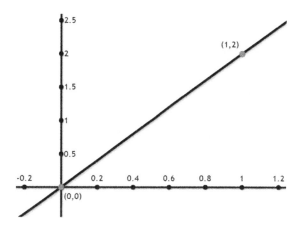

Graphing Lines Using Standard Form

1)
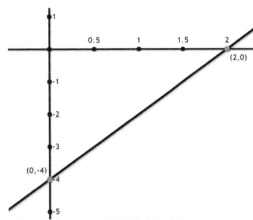

2)
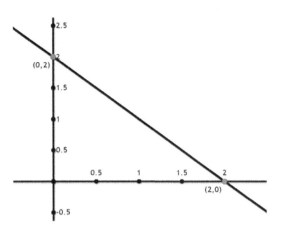

Writing Linear Equations

1) $y = 7x + 26$

2) $y = \dfrac{1}{9}x + \dfrac{31}{9}$

3) $y = -x - 2$

4) $y = -5x - 4$

5) $y = x + 3$

6) $y = -5x + 2$

7) $y = 2x - 5$

8) $y = 4$

9) $y = -2x + 1$

10) $y = 3x - 1$

11) $y = -x - 2$

12) $y = 4x - 9$

13) $y = 9x - 32$

14) $y = -2x + 3$

15) $y = \dfrac{8}{3}x - \dfrac{25}{3}$

16) $y = -\dfrac{3}{4}x - \dfrac{7}{2}$

17) $y = \dfrac{1}{4}x - \dfrac{5}{4}$

18) $y = -\dfrac{4}{3}x + \dfrac{19}{3}$

Graphing Linear Inequalities

1)

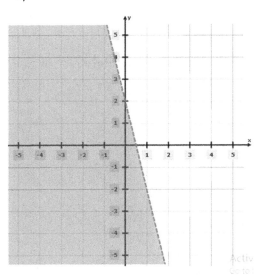

2)

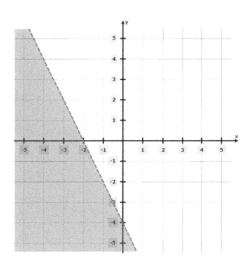

4)

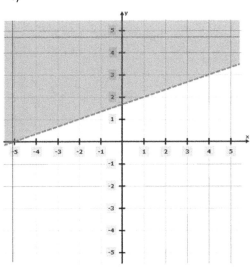

5)

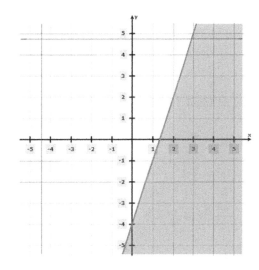

Finding Midpoint

1) (2.5, −3.5)
2) (−1, −2)
3) (8, 1.5)
4) (2, 1.5)
5) (1, −4)
6) (0.5, −4.5)

7) (0, 2.5)
8) (−2.5, 2)
9) (2, −2)
10) (0.05, −0.9)
11) (4.05, 5.96)
12) (−2, − 0.5)

13) $(\frac{1}{2}, 1\frac{1}{2})$
14) (−4, 1)
15) (1.25, 2.5)
16) $(2, \frac{3}{2})$

Finding Distance of Two Points

1) 1
2) 7.1
3) 6.32
4) 4
5) 12.21
6) 4.12

7) 3.61
8) 12.1
9) 5.66
10) 11.04
11) 4.47
12) 17.03

13) 10.77
14) 8.25
15) 16.4
16) 10.3
17) 4.47
18) 12.1

Slope–intercept form

1) $y = 14x + 7$
2) $y = -2x - 14$
3) $y = -\frac{11}{7}x + 8$
4) $y = -\frac{9}{5}x - 7$
5) $y = \frac{x}{3} - 2$
6) $y = \frac{13}{11}x + \frac{12}{11}$

7) $y = \frac{11}{8}x + 6$
8) $y = \frac{3}{2}x + 8$
9) $y = -3x - 4$
10) $y = -2x + 5$
11) $y = -x - 2$
12) $y = -\frac{6}{5}x - 3$

Equations of horizontal and vertical lines

1) $y = 0$ (it is on x axes)

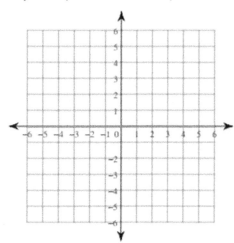

2) $y = 2$

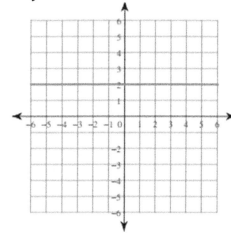

3) $x = -4$

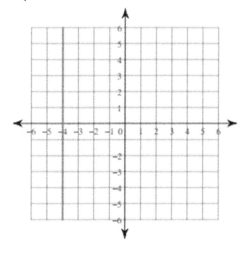

4) $x = 3$

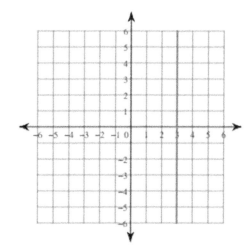

Equation of parallel or perpendicular lines

1) $y = -\dfrac{4}{7}x - \dfrac{36}{7}$

2) $y = -x - 2$

3) $y = 2x + 9$

4) $y = 3x + 30$

5) $y = -\dfrac{3}{5}x + 2$

6) $y = 6x + 1$

7) $y = \dfrac{1}{5}x - \dfrac{17}{5}$

8) $y = \dfrac{6}{5}x + \dfrac{14}{5}$

9) $y = -\dfrac{5}{2}x + \dfrac{9}{2}$

10) $y = -\dfrac{2}{3}x + \dfrac{1}{3}$

11) $y = 4x - 3$

12) $y = -\dfrac{6}{5}x + \dfrac{7}{5}$

13) $x = 2$

14) $y = 3$

15) $y = -8x + 3$

16) $y = \dfrac{1}{2}x + \dfrac{5}{2}$

17) $y = -\dfrac{9}{5}x - 4$

18) $y = -x + 3$

Chapter 10: Polynomials

Topics that you'll learn in this chapter:

✓ Simplifying Polynomials

✓ Multiplying Monomials

✓ Multiplying and Dividing Monomials

✓ Multiplying a Polynomial and a Monomial

✓ Multiplying Binomials

✓ Factoring Trinomials

✓ Operations with Polynomials

✓ Solving Quadratic Equations

Mathematics – the unshaken Foundation of Sciences, and the plentiful Fountain of Advantage to human affairs. — *Isaac Barrow*

Helpful	1– Find "like" terms. (they have same variables with same power).	**Example:**
Hints	2– Add or Subtract "like" terms using PEMDAS operation.	$2x^5 - 3x^3 + 8x^2 - 2x^5 =$ $-3x^3 + 8x^2$

Simplifying Polynomials

✎ *Simplify each expression.*

1) $11 - 4x^2 + 3x^2 - 7x^3 + 3$

2) $2x^5 - x^3 + 8x^2 - 2x^5$

3) $(-5)(x^6 + 10) - 8(14 - x^6)$

4) $4(2x^2 + 4x^2 - 3x^3) + 6x^3 + 17$

5) $11 - 6x^2 + 5x^2 - 12x^3 + 22$

6) $2x^2 - 2x + 3x^3 + 12x - 22x$

7) $(3x - 8)(3x - 4)$

8) $(12x + 2y)^2$

9) $(12x^3 + 28x^2 + 10x + 4) \div (x + 2)$

10) $(2x + 12x^2 - 2) \div (2x + 1)$

11) $(2x^3 - 1) + (3x^3 - 2x^3)$

12) $(x - 5)(x - 3)$

13) $(3x + 8)(3x - 8)$

14) $(8x^2 - 3x) - (5x - 5 - 8x^2)$

Multiplying Monomials

Helpful *Hints*	A monomial is a polynomial with just one term, like $2x$ or $7y$.	**Example:** $2u^3 \times (-3u)$ $= -6u^4$

✎ **Simplify each expression.**

1) $2xy^2z \times 4z^2$

2) $4xy \times x^2y$

3) $4pq^3 \times (-2p^4q)$

4) $8s^4t^2 \times st^5$

5) $12p^3 \times (-3p^4)$

6) $-4p^2q^3r \times 6pq^2r^3$

7) $(-8a^4) \times (-12a^6b)$

8) $3u^4v^2 \times (-7u^2v^3)$

9) $4u^3 \times (-2u)$

10) $-6xy^2 \times 3x^2y$

11) $12y^2z^3 \times (-y^2z)$

12) $5a^2bc^2 \times 2abc^2$

Multiplying and Dividing Monomials

Helpful

Hints

- When you divide two monomials you need to divide their coefficients and then divide their variables.
- In case of exponents with the same base, you need to subtract their powers.

Example:

$$(-3x^2)(8x^4y^{12}) = -24x^6y^{12}$$

$$\frac{36\,x^5y^7}{4\,x^4y^5} = 9xy^2$$

✎ *Simplify.*

1) $(7x^4y^6)(4x^3y^4)$

2) $(15x^4)\,(3x^9)$

3) $(12x^2y^9)(7x^9y^{12})$

4) $\dfrac{80\ ^{12}y^9}{10x^6y^7}$

5) $\dfrac{95\ ^{18}y^7}{5x^9y^2}$

6) $\dfrac{20\ ^3y^8}{40\ ^3y^7}$

7) $\dfrac{-15x^{17}y^{13}}{3x^6y^9}$

8) $\dfrac{-64x^8y^{10}}{8x^3y^7}$

Multiplying a Polynomial and a Monomial

Helpful	– When multiplying monomials, use the product rule for exponents.	**Example:**
Hints	– When multiplying a monomial by a polynomial, use the distributive property.	$2x\,(8x-2) =$
	$a \times (b+c) = a \times b + a \times c$	$16x^2 - 4x$

✎ *Find each product.*

1) $5\,(3x - 6y)$

2) $9x\,(2x + 4y)$

3) $8x\,(7x - 4)$

4) $12x\,(3x + 9)$

5) $11x\,(2x - 11y)$

6) $2x\,(6x - 6y)$

7) $3x\,(2x^2 - 3x + 8)$

8) $13x\,(4x + 8y)$

9) $20\,(2x^2 - 8x - 5)$

10) $3x\,(3x - 2)$

11) $6x^3\,(3x^2 - 2x + 2)$

12) $8x^2\,(3x^2 - 5xy + 7y^2)$

13) $2x^2\,(3x^2 - 5x + 12)$

14) $2x^3\,(2x^2 + 5x - 4)$

15) $5x\,(6x^2 - 5xy + 2y^2)$

16) $9\,(x^2 + xy - 8y^2)$

Multiplying Binomials

Helpful *Hints*	Use "FOIL". (First–Out–In–Last) $(x + a)(x + b) = x^2 + (b + a)x + ab$	**Example:** $(x + 2)(x - 3) =$ $x^2 - x - 6$

✎ **Multiply.**

1) $(3x - 2)(4x + 2)$

2) $(2x - 5)(x + 7)$

3) $(x + 2)(x + 8)$

4) $(x^2 + 2)(x^2 - 2)$

5) $(x - 2)(x + 4)$

6) $(x - 8)(2x + 8)$

7) $(5x - 4)(3x + 3)$

8) $(x - 7)(x - 6)$

9) $(6x + 9)(4x + 9)$

10) $(2x - 6)(5x + 6)$

11) $(x - 7)(x + 7)$

12) $(x + 4)(4x - 8)$

13) $(6x - 4)(6x + 4)$

14) $(x - 7)(x + 2)$

15) $(x - 8)(x + 8)$

16) $(3x + 3)(3x - 4)$

17) $(x + 3)(x + 3)$

18) $(x + 4)(x + 6)$

Factoring Trinomials

Helpful	"FOIL"	**Example:**
	$(x + a)(x + b) = x^2 + (b + a)x + ab$	$x^2 + 5x + 6 =$
Hints	"Difference of Squares"	$(x + 2)(x + 3)$
	$a^2 - b^2 = (a + b)(a - b)$	
	$a^2 + 2ab + b^2 = (a + b)(a + b)$	
	$a^2 - 2ab + b^2 = (a - b)(a - b)$	
	"Reverse FOIL"	
	$x^2 + (b + a)x + ab = (x + a)(x + b)$	

✎ *Factor each trinomial.*

1) $x^2 - 7x + 12$

2) $x^2 + 5x - 14$

3) $x^2 - 11x - 42$

4) $6x^2 + x - 12$

5) $x^2 - 17x + 30$

6) $x^2 + 8x + 15$

7) $3x^2 + 11x - 4$

8) $x^2 - 6x - 27$

9) $10x^2 + 33x - 7$

10) $x^2 + 24x + 144$

11) $49x^2 + 28xy + 4y^2$

12) $16x^2 - 40x + 25$

13) $x^2 - 10x + 25$

14) $25x^2 - 20x + 4$

15) $x^3 + 6x^2y^2 + 9xy^3$

16) $9x^2 + 24x + 16$

17) $x^2 - 8x + 16$

18) $x^2 + 121 + 22x$

Operations with Polynomials

Helpful	– When multiplying a monomial by a polynomial, use the distributive property.	**Example:**
Hints	$a \times (b + c) = a \times b + a \times c$	$5(6x - 1) =$ $30x - 5$

✎ *Find each product.*

1) $3x^2 (6x - 5)$

2) $5x^2 (7x - 2)$

3) $-3 (8x - 3)$

4) $6x^3 (-3x + 4)$

5) $9 (6x + 2)$

6) $8 (3x + 7)$

7) $5 (6x - 1)$

8) $-7x^4 (2x - 4)$

9) $8 (x^2 + 2x - 3)$

10) $4 (4x^2 - 2x + 1)$

11) $2 (3x^2 + 2x - 2)$

12) $8x (5x^2 + 3x + 8)$

13) $(9x + 1)(3x - 1)$

14) $(4x + 5)(6x - 5)$

15) $(7x + 3)(5x - 6)$

16) $(3x - 4)(3x + 8)$

Solving Quadratic Equations

$Helpful$	Write the equation in the form of $ax^2 + bx + c = 0$ Factorize the quadratic.
$Hints$	Use quadratic formula if you couldn't factorize the quadratic.

Quadratic formula

$$x = \frac{-b \pm \sqrt{b^2 - 4ac}}{2a}$$

✎ *Solve each equation by factoring or by using the quadratic formula.*

1) $x^2 + x - 20 = 2x$

2) $x^2 + 8x = -15$

3) $7x^2 - 14x = -7$

4) $6x^2 - 18x - 18 = 6$

5) $2x^2 + 6x - 24 = 12$

6) $2x^2 - 22x + 38 = -10$

7) $(2x + 5)(4x + 3) = 0$

8) $(x + 2)(x - 7) = 0$

9) $(x + 3)(x + 5) = 0$

10) $(5x + 7)(x + 4) = 0$

11) $-4x^2 - 8x - 3 = -3 - 5x^2$

12) $10x^2 = 27x - 18$

13) $7x^2 - 6x + 3 = 3$

14) $x^2 = 2x$

15) $2x^2 - 14 = -3x$

16) $10x^2 - 26x = -12$

17) $15x^2 + 80 = -80x$

18) $x^2 + 15x = -56$

Answers of Worksheets – Chapter 10

Simplifying Polynomials

1) $-7x^3 - x^2 + 14$

2) $-x^3 + 8x^2$

3) $3x^6 - 162$

4) $-6x^3 + 24x^2 + 17$

5) $-12x^3 - x^2 + 33$

6) $3x^3 + 2x^2 - 12x$

7) $9x^2 - 36x + 32$

8) $144x^2 + 48xy + 4y^2$

9) $12x^2 + 4x + 2$

10) $6x - 1$

11) $3x^3 - 1$

12) $x^2 - 8x + 15$

13) $9x^2 - 64$

14) $16x^2 - 8x + 5$

Multiplying Monomials

1) $8xy^2z^3$

2) $4x^3y^2$

3) $-8p^5q^4$

4) $8s^5t^7$

5) $-36p^7$

6) $-24p^3q^5r^4$

7) $96a^{10}b$

8) $-21u^6v^5$

9) $-8u^4$

10) $-18x^3y^3$

11) $-12y^4z^4$

12) $10a^3b^2c^4$

Multiplying and Dividing Monomials

1) $28x^7y^{10}$

2) $45x^{13}$

3) $84x^{11}y^{21}$

4) $8x^6y^2$

5) $19x^9y^5$

6) $5y$

7) $-5x^{11}y^4$

8) $-8x^5y^3$

Multiplying a Polynomial and a Monomial

1) $15x - 30y$

2) $18x^2 + 36xy$

3) $56x^2 - 32x$

4) $36x^2 + 108x$

5) $22x^2 - 121xy$

6) $12x^2 - 12xy$

7) $6x^3 - 9x^2 + 24x$

8) $52x^2 + 104xy$

9) $40x^2 - 160x - 100$

10) $9x^2 - 6x$

11) $18x^5 - 12x^4 + 12x^3$

12) $24x^4 - 40x^3y + 56y^2x^2$

13) $6x^4 - 10x^3 + 24x^2$

14) $4x^5 + 10x^4 - 8x^3$

15) $30x^3 - 25x^2y + 10xy^2$

16) $9x^2 + 9xy - 72y^2$

Multiplying Binomials

1) $12x^2 - 2x - 4$

2) $2x^2 + 9x - 35$

3) $x^2 + 10x + 16$

4) $x^4 - 4$

5) $x^2 + 2x - 8$

6) $2x^2 - 8x - 64$

7) $15x^2 + 3x - 12$

8) $x^2 - 13x + 42$

9) $24x^2 + 90x + 81$

10) $10x^2 - 18x - 36$

11) $x^2 - 49$

12) $4x^2 + 8x - 32$

13) $36x^2 - 16$

14) $x^2 - 5x - 14$

15) $x^2 - 64$

16) $9x^2 - 3x - 12$

17) $x^2 + 6x + 9$

18) $x^2 + 10x + 24$

Factoring Trinomials

1) $(x - 3)(x - 4)$

2) $(x - 2)(x + 7)$

3) $(x + 3)(x - 14)$

4) $(2x + 3)(3x - 4)$

5) $(x - 15)(x - 2)$

6) $(x + 3)(x + 5)$

7) $(3x - 1)(x + 4)$

8) $(x - 9)(x + 3)$

9) $(5x - 1)(2x + 7)$

10) $(x + 12)(x + 12)$

11) $(7x + 2y)(7x + 2y)$

12) $(4x - 5)(4x - 5)$

13) $(x - 5)(x - 5)$

14) $(5x - 2)(5x - 2)$

15) $x(x^2 + 6xy^2 + 9y^3)$

16) $(3x + 4)(3x + 4)$

17) $(x - 4)(x - 4)$

18) $(x + 11)(x + 11)$

Operations with Polynomials

1) $18x^3 - 15x^2$

2) $35x^3 - 10x^2$

3) $-24x + 9$

4) $-18x^4 + 24x^3$

5) $54x + 18$

6) $24x + 56$

7) $30x - 5$

8) $-14x^5 + 28x^4$

9) $8x^2 + 16x - 24$

10) $16x^2 - 8x + 4$

11) $6x^2 + 4x - 4$

12) $40x^3 + 24x^2 + 64x$

13) $27x^2 - 6x - 1$

14) $24x^2 + 10x - 25$

15) $35x^2 - 27x - 18$

16) $9x^2 + 12x - 32$

Solving Quadratic Equations

1) $\{5, -4\}$

2) $\{-5, -3\}$

3) $\{1\}$

4) $\{4, -1\}$

5) $\{3, -6\}$

6) $\{3, 8\}$

7) $\{-\frac{5}{2}, -\frac{3}{4}\}$

8) $\{-2, 7\}$

9) $\{-3, -5\}$

10) $\{-\frac{7}{5}, -4\}$

11) $\{8, 0\}$

12) $\{\frac{6}{5}, \frac{3}{2}\}$

13) $\{\frac{6}{7}, 0\}$

14) $\{2, 0\}$

15) $\{-\frac{7}{2}, 2\}$

16) $\{\frac{3}{5}, 2\}$

17) $\{-\frac{4}{3}, -4\}$

18) $\{-8, -7\}$

Chapter 11: Exponents and Radicals

Topics that you'll learn in this chapter:

✓ Multiplication Property of Exponents

✓ Division Property of Exponents

✓ Powers of Products and Quotients

✓ Zero and Negative Exponents

✓ Negative Exponents and Negative Bases

✓ Writing Scientific Notation

✓ Square Roots

Mathematics is no more computation than typing is literature.

– John Allen Paulos

Multiplication Property of Exponents

Helpful	**Exponents rules**	**Example:**
Hints	$x^a \cdot x^b = x^{a+b}$ $\quad$ $\dfrac{x^a}{x^b} = x^{a-b}$	$(x^2y)^3 = x^6y^3$
	$\dfrac{1}{x^b} = x^{-b}$ $\quad$ $(x^a)^b = x^{a.b}$	
	$(xy)^a = x^a \cdot y^a$	

✎ *Simplify.*

1) $4^2 \cdot 4^2$

2) $2 \cdot 2^2 \cdot 2^2$

3) $3^2 \cdot 3^2$

4) $3x^3 \cdot x$

5) $12x^4 \cdot 3x$

6) $6x \cdot 2x^2$

7) $5x^4 \cdot 5x^4$

8) $6x^2 \cdot 6x^3y^4$

9) $7x^2y^5 \cdot 9xy^3$

10) $7xy^4 \cdot 4x^3y^3$

11) $(2x^2)^2$

12) $3x^5y^3 \cdot 8x^2y^3$

13) $7x^3 \cdot 10y^3x^5 \cdot 8yx^3$

14) $(x^4)^3$

15) $(2x^2)^4$

16) $(x^2)^3$

17) $(6x)^2$

18) $3x^4y^5 \cdot 7x^2y^3$

Division Property of Exponents

Helpful	$\frac{x^a}{x^b} = x^{a-b}$, $x \neq 0$	**Example:**
Hints		$\frac{x^{12}}{x^5} = x^7$

✎ **Simplify.**

1) $\frac{5^5}{5}$

2) $\frac{3}{3^5}$

3) $\frac{2^2}{2^3}$

4) $\frac{2^4}{2^2}$

5) $\frac{x}{x^3}$

6) $\frac{3x^3}{9x^4}$

7) $\frac{2x^{-5}}{9x^{-2}}$

8) $\frac{21x^8}{7x^3}$

9) $\frac{7x^6}{4x^7}$

10) $\frac{6x^2}{4x^3}$

11) $\frac{5x}{10^3}$

12) $\frac{3x^3}{2x^5}$

13) $\frac{12x^3}{14^6}$

14) $\frac{12^3}{9y^8}$

15) $\frac{25xy^4}{5x^6y^2}$

16) $\frac{2x^4}{7x}$

17) $\frac{16^2y^8}{4x^3}$

18) $\frac{12^4}{15x^7y^9}$

19) $\frac{12yx^4}{10yx^8}$

20) $\frac{16^4y}{9x^8y^2}$

21) $\frac{5x^8}{20^8}$

Powers of Products and Quotients

Helpful	For any nonzero numbers a and b and any integer $(ab)^x = a^x b^x$	**Example:**
Hints		$(2x^2 \cdot y^3)^2 =$ $4x^2 \cdot y^6$

✍ *Simplify.*

1) $(2x^3)^4$

2) $(4xy^4)^2$

3) $(5x^4)^2$

4) $(11x^5)^2$

5) $(4x^2y^4)^4$

6) $(2x^4y^4)^3$

7) $(3x^2y^2)^2$

8) $(3x^4y^3)^4$

9) $(2x^6y^8)^2$

10) $(12x \ 3x)^3$

11) $(2x^9 \ x^6)^3$

12) $(5x^{10}y^3)^3$

13) $(4x^3 \ x^2)^2$

14) $(3x^3 \ 5x)^2$

15) $(10x^{11}y^3)^2$

16) $(9x^7 \ y^5)^2$

17) $(4x^4y^6)^5$

18) $(4x^4)^2$

19) $(3x \ 4y^3)^2$

20) $(9x^2y)^3$

21) $(12x^2y^5)^2$

Zero and Negative Exponents

Helpful Hints	A negative exponent simply means that the base is on the wrong side of the fraction line, so you need to flip the base to the other side. For instance, "x^{-2}" (pronounced as "ecks to the minus two") just means "x^2" but underneath, as in $\frac{1}{x^2}$	**Example:** $5^{-2} = \frac{1}{25}$

✎ *Evaluate the following expressions.*

1) 8^{-2}

2) 2^{-4}

3) 10^{-2}

4) 5^{-3}

5) 22^{-1}

6) 9^{-1}

7) 3^{-2}

8) 4^{-2}

9) 5^{-2}

10) 35^{-1}

11) 6^{-3}

12) 0^{15}

13) 10^{-9}

14) 3^{-4}

15) 5^{-2}

16) 2^{-3}

17) 3^{-3}

18) 8^{-1}

19) 7^{-3}

20) 6^{-2}

21) $\left(\frac{2}{3}\right)^{-2}$

22) $\left(\frac{1}{5}\right)^{-3}$

23) $\left(\frac{1}{2}\right)^{-8}$

24) $\left(\frac{2}{5}\right)^{-3}$

25) 10^{-3}

26) 1^{-10}

Negative Exponents and Negative Bases

Helpful	– Make the power positive. A negative exponent is the reciprocal of that number with a positive exponent.	**Example:**
Hints	– The parenthesis is important! – 5^{-2} is not the same as $(-5)^{-2}$ $-5^{-2} = -\dfrac{1}{5^2}$ and $(-5)^{-2} = +\dfrac{1}{5^2}$	$2x^{-3} = \dfrac{2}{x^3}$

✎ *Simplify.*

1) -6^{-1}

2) $-4x^{-3}$

3) $-\dfrac{5x}{x^{-3}}$

4) $-\dfrac{a^{-3}}{b^{-2}}$

5) $-\dfrac{5}{x^{-3}}$

6) $\dfrac{7b}{-9^{-4}}$

7) $-\dfrac{5n^{-2}}{10p^{-3}}$

8) $\dfrac{4ab^{-2}}{-3c^{-2}}$

9) $-12x^2y^{-3}$

10) $\left(-\dfrac{1}{3}\right)^{-2}$

11) $\left(-\dfrac{3}{4}\right)^{-2}$

12) $\left(\dfrac{3a}{2c}\right)^{-2}$

13) $\left(-\dfrac{5x}{3yz}\right)^{-3}$

14) $-\dfrac{2x}{a^{-4}}$

Writing Scientific Notation

Helpful

Hints

– It is used to write very big or very small numbers in decimal form.

– In scientific notation all numbers are written in the form of:

$$m \times 10^n$$

Decimal notation	Scientific notation
5	5×10^0
−25,000	$−2.5 \times 10^4$
0.5	5×10^{-1}
2,122.456	$2,122456 \times 10^3$

✍ *Write each number in scientific notation.*

1) 91×10^3

2) 60

3) 2000000

4) 0.0000006

5) 354000

6) 0.000325

7) 2.5

8) 0.00023

9) 56000000

10) 2000000

11) 78000000

12) 0.0000022

13) 0.00012

14) 0.004

15) 78

16) 1600

17) 1450

18) 130000

19) 60

20) 0.113

21) 0.02

Square Roots

Helpful	$-$ A square root of x is a number r whose square is: $r^2 = x$	Example:
Hints	r is a square root of x.	$\sqrt{4} = 2$

✍ *Find the value each square root.*

1) $\sqrt{1}$ 8) $\sqrt{0}$ 15) $\sqrt{256}$

2) $\sqrt{4}$ 9) $\sqrt{64}$ 16) $\sqrt{289}$

3) $\sqrt{9}$ 10) $\sqrt{81}$ 17) $\sqrt{324}$

4) $\sqrt{25}$ 11) $\sqrt{121}$ 18) $\sqrt{400}$

5) $\sqrt{16}$ 12) $\sqrt{225}$ 19) $\sqrt{900}$

6) $\sqrt{49}$ 13) $\sqrt{144}$ 20) $\sqrt{529}$

7) $\sqrt{36}$ 14) $\sqrt{100}$ 21) $\sqrt{90}$

Answers of Worksheets – Chapter 11

Multiplication Property of Exponents

1) 4^4

2) 2^5

3) 3^4

4) $3x^4$

5) $36x^5$

6) $12x^3$

7) $25x^8$

8) $36x^5y^4$

9) $63x^3y^8$

10) $28x^4y^7$

11) $4x^4$

12) $24x^7y^6$

13) $560x^{11}y^4$

14) x^{12}

15) $16x^8$

16) x^6

17) $36x^2$

18) $21x^6y^8$

Division Property of Exponents

1) 5^4

2) $\frac{1}{3^4}$

3) $\frac{1}{2}$

4) 2^2

5) $\frac{1}{x^2}$

6) $\frac{1}{3x}$

7) $\frac{2}{9x^3}$

8) $3x^5$

9) $\frac{7}{4x}$

10) $\frac{3}{2x}$

11) $\frac{1}{2x^2}$

12) $\frac{3}{2x^2}$

13) $\frac{6}{7x^3}$

14) $\frac{4x^3}{3y^8}$

15) $\frac{5y^2}{x^5}$

16) $\frac{2x^3}{7}$

17) $\frac{4y^8}{x}$

18) $\frac{4}{5x^3y^9}$

19) $\frac{6}{5x^4}$

20) $\frac{16}{9x^4y}$

21) $\frac{1}{4}$

Powers of Products and Quotients

1) $16x^{12}$

2) $16x^2y^8$

3) $25x^8$

4) $121x^{10}$

5) $256x^8y^{16}$

6) $8x^{12}y^{12}$

7) $9x^4y^4$

8) $81x^{16}y^{12}$

9) $4x^{12}y^{16}$

10) $46,656x^6$

11) $8x^{45}$

12) $125x^{30}y^9$

13) $16x^{10}$

14) $225x^8$

15) $100x^{22}y^6$

16) $81x^{14}y^{10}$

17) $1,024x^{20}y^{30}$

18) $16x^8$

19) $144x^2y^6$ 20) $729x^6y^3$ 21) $144x^4y^{10}$

Zero and Negative Exponents

1) $\frac{1}{64}$

2) $\frac{1}{16}$

3) $\frac{1}{100}$

4) $\frac{1}{125}$

5) $\frac{1}{22}$

6) $\frac{1}{9}$

7) $\frac{1}{9}$

8) $\frac{1}{16}$

9) $\frac{1}{25}$

10) $\frac{1}{35}$

11) $\frac{1}{216}$

12) 0

13) $\frac{1}{1000000000}$

14) $\frac{1}{81}$

15) $\frac{1}{25}$

16) $\frac{1}{8}$

17) $\frac{1}{27}$

18) $\frac{1}{8}$

19) $\frac{1}{343}$

20) $\frac{1}{36}$

21) $\frac{9}{4}$

22) 125

23) 256

24) $\frac{125}{8}$

25) $\frac{1}{1000}$

26) 1

Negative Exponents and Negative Bases

1) $-\frac{1}{6}$

2) $-\frac{4}{x^3}$

3) $-5x^4$

4) $-\frac{b^2}{a^3}$

5) $-5x^3$

6) $-\frac{7bc^4}{9}$

7) $-\frac{p^3}{2n^2}$

8) $-\frac{4ac^2}{3b^2}$

9) $-\frac{12x^2}{y^3}$

10) 9

11) $\frac{16}{9}$

12) $\frac{4c^2}{9a^2}$

13) $-\frac{27\ ^3z^3}{125x^3}$

14) $-2xa^4$

Writing Scientific Notation

1) 9.1×10^4

2) 6×10^1

3) 2×10^6

4) 6×10^{-7}

5) 3.54×10^5

6) 3.25×10^{-4}

7) 2.5×10^0

8) 2.3×10^{-4}

9) 5.6×10^7

10) 2×10^6

11) 7.8×10^7

12) 2.2×10^{-6}

13) 1.2×10^{-4}

14) 4×10^{-3}

15) 7.8×10^{1}

16) 1.6×10^{3}

17) 1.45×10^{3}

18) 1.3×10^{5}

19) 6×10^{1}

20) 1.13×10^{-1}

21) 2×10^{-2}

Square Roots

1) 1

2) 2

3) 3

4) 5

5) 4

6) 7

7) 6

8) 0

9) 8

10) 9

11) 11

12) 15

13) 12

14) 10

15) 16

16) 17

17) 18

18) 20

19) 30

20) 23

21) $3\sqrt{10}$

Chapter 12: Geometry

Topics that you'll learn in this chapter:

✓ The Pythagorean Theorem

✓ Area of Triangles

✓ Perimeter of Polygons

✓ Area and Circumference of Circles

✓ Area of Squares, Rectangles, and Parallelograms

✓ Area of Trapezoids

Mathematics is, as it were, a sensuous logic, and relates to philosophy as do the arts, music, and plastic art to poetry. — K. Shegel

The Pythagorean Theorem

Helpful

Hints

− In any right triangle:

$a^2 + b^2 = c^2$

Example:

Missing side = 6

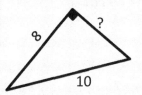

🖎*Do the following lengths form a right triangle?*

1)

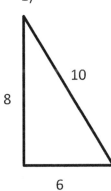

2)

3)

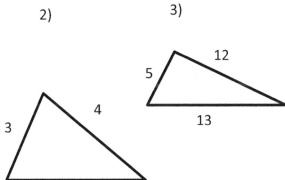

🖎*Find each missing length to the nearest tenth.*

4)

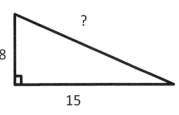

5)

6)

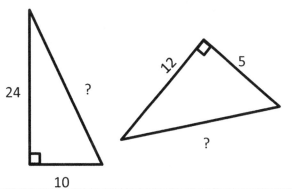

Area of Triangles

Helpful

Area $= \frac{1}{2}$ (*base* $\times$ *height*)

Hints

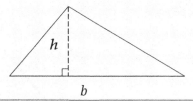

✏️ *Find the area of each.*

1)

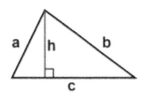

c = 9 mi

h = 3.7 mi

2)

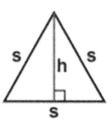

s = 14 m

h = 12.2 m

3)

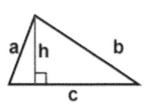

a = 5 m

b = 11 m

c = 14 m

h = 4 m

4)

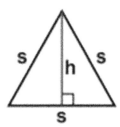

s = 10 m

h = 8.6 m

Perimeter of Polygons

Helpful

Hints

Perimeter of a square = 4s

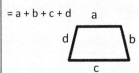 s

Perimeter of a rectangle

= 2(*l* + *w*)

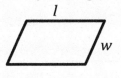 w

l

Perimeter of trapezoid

= a + b + c + d

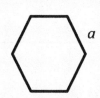
a
d   b
c

Perimeter of Pentagon = 6a

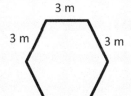 a

Perimeter of a parallelogram = 2(l + w)

l

w

Example:

P = 18

3 m

3 m   3 m

Find the perimeter of each shape.

1)
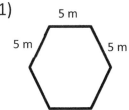
5 m
5 m   5 m

2)
15 mm
15 mm   15mm
15 mm

3)
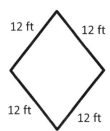
12 ft   12 ft

12 ft   12 ft

4)
18 in
12 in   12 in
18 in

Area and Circumference of Circles

Area = πr^2

Circumference = $2\pi r$

Example:

If the radius of a circle is 3, then:

Area = 28.27

Circumference = 18.85

✎ *Find the area and circumference of each.* ($\pi = 3.14$)

1)

2)

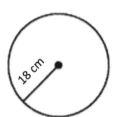

3)

4)

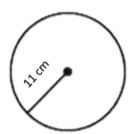

5)

6)

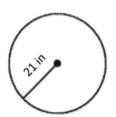

Area of Squares, Rectangles, and Parallelograms

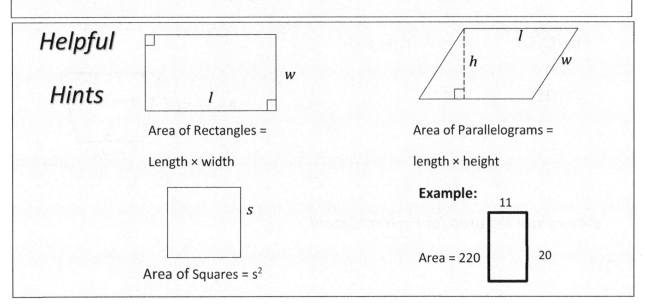

Helpful

Hints

Area of Rectangles =

Length × width

Area of Squares = s²

Area of Parallelograms =

length × height

Example:

Area = 220

✎ **Find the area of each.**

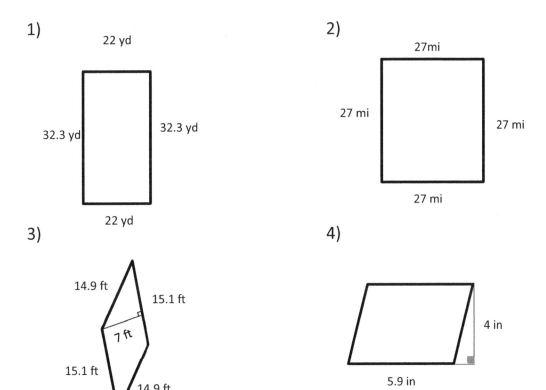

1)

22 yd

32.3 yd   32.3 yd

22 yd

2)

27mi

27 mi   27 mi

27 mi

3)

14.9 ft

15.1 ft

7 ft

15.1 ft

14.9 ft

4)

4 in

5.9 in

Area of Trapezoids

Helpful $A = \frac{1}{2}h(b_1 + b_2)$

Example:

Hints

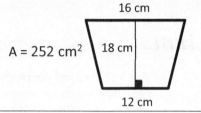

A = 252 cm²

16 cm

18 cm

12 cm

Calculate the area for each trapezoid.

1)

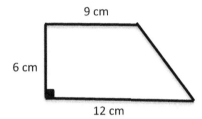

9 cm

6 cm

12 cm

2)

14 m

10 m

18 m

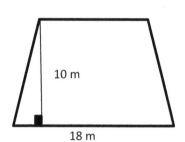

3)

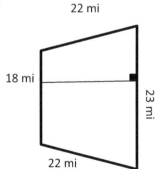

22 mi

18 mi

23 mi

22 mi

4)

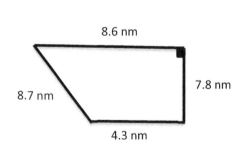

8.6 nm

8.7 nm

7.8 nm

4.3 nm

Answers of Worksheets – Chapter 12

The Pythagorean Theorem

1) yes
2) yes
3) yes

4) 17
5) 26
6) 13

Area of Triangles

1) 16.65 mi^2
2) 85.4 m^2

3) 28 m^2
4) 43 m^2

Perimeter of Polygons

1) 30 m
2) 60 mm

3) 48 ft
4) 60 in

Area and Circumference of Circles

1) Area: 50.24 in^2, Circumference: 25.12 in
2) Area: 1,017.36 cm^2, Circumference: 113.04 cm
3) Area: 78.5m^2, Circumference: 31.4 m
4) Area: 379.94 cm^2, Circumference: 69.08 cm
5) Area: 200.96 km^2, Circumference: 50.2 km
6) Area: 1,384.74 km^2, Circumference: 131.88 km

Area of Squares, Rectangles, and Parallelograms

1) 710.6 yd^2
2) 729 mi^2

3) 105.7 ft^2
4) 23.6 in^2

Area of Trapezoids

1) 63 cm^2
2) 160 m^2

3) 410 mi^2
4) 50.31 nm^2

Chapter 13: Solid Figures

Topics that you'll learn in this chapter:

✓ Volume of Cubes

✓ Volume of Rectangle Prisms

✓ Surface Area of Cubes

✓ Surface Area of Rectangle Prisms

✓ Volume of a Cylinder

✓ Surface Area of a Cylinder

Mathematics is a great motivator for all humans. Because its career starts with zero and it never end (infinity)

Volume of Cubes

Helpful	– Volume is the measure of the amount of space inside of a solid figure, like a cube, ball, cylinder or pyramid.
Hints	– Volume of a cube = (one side)^3
	– Volume of a rectangle prism: Length × Width × Height

✎*Find the volume of each.*

1)
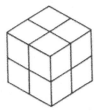

2)

3)
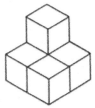

4)
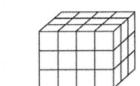

5)
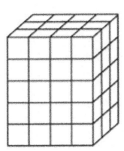

6)
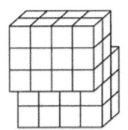

Volume of Rectangle Prisms

Helpful	Volume of rectangle prism	**Example:**
Hints	length × width × height	$10 \times 5 \times 8 = 400m^3$ 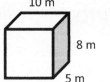

✎*Find the volume of each of the rectangular prisms.*

1)

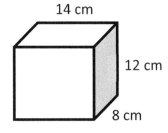

2)

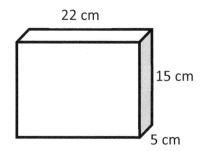

3)

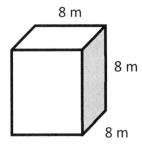

4)

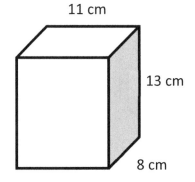

Surface Area of Cubes

✎ *Find the surface of each cube.*

1)

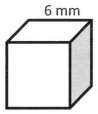

6 mm

2)

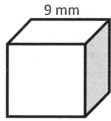

9 mm

3)

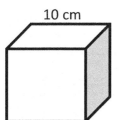

10 cm

4)

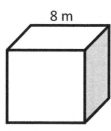

8 m

5)

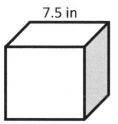

7.5 in

6)

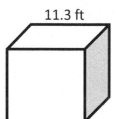

11.3 ft

Surface Area of a Rectangle Prism

Helpful	Surface Area of a Rectangle Prism Formula:
Hints	SA =2 [(width × length) + (height × length) + width × height)]

✎ **Find the surface of each prism.**

1)

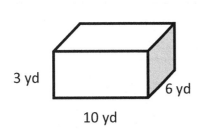

3 yd
6 yd
10 yd

2)

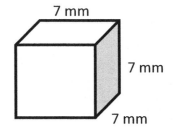

7 mm
7 mm
7 mm

3)

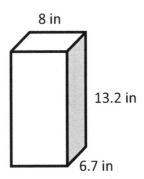

8 in
13.2 in
6.7 in

4)

17 cm

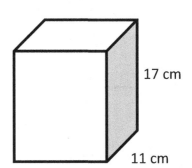

17 cm
11 cm

Volume of a Cylinder

✎ **Find the volume of each cylinder.** (π = 3.14)

1)

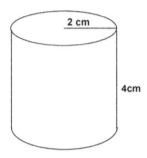

2 cm

4cm

2)

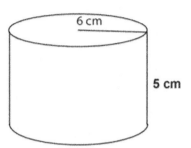

6 cm

5 cm

3)

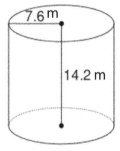

7.6 m

14.2 m

4)

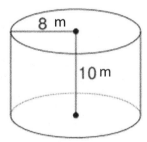

8 m

10 m

Surface Area of a Cylinder

Helpful

Hints

Surface area of a cylinder

SA = 2πr² + 2πrh

Example:

Surface area

= 1727

14 m

11 m

✎ ***Find the surface of each cylinder.*** (π = 3.14)

1)

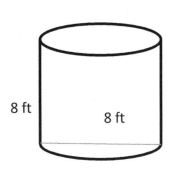

8 ft

8 ft

2)

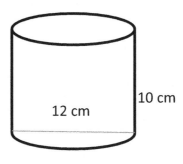

12 cm

10 cm

3)

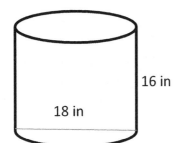

16 in

18 in

4)

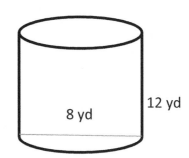

8 yd

12 yd

Answers of Worksheets – Chapter 13

Volumes of Cubes

1) 8
2) 4
3) 5
4) 36
5) 60
6) 44

Volume of Rectangle Prisms

1) 1344 cm^3
2) 1650 cm^3
3) 512 m^3
4) 1144 cm^3

Surface Area of a Cube

1) 216 mm^2
2) 486 mm^2
3) 600 cm^2
4) 384 m^2
5) 337.5 in^2
6) 766.14 ft^2

Surface Area of a Prism

1) 216 yd^2
2) 294 mm^2
3) 495.28 in^2
4) 1326 cm^2

Volume of a Cylinder

1) 50.24 cm^3
2) 565.2 cm^3
3) 2,575.403 m^3
4) 2009.6 m^3

Surface Area of a Cylinder

1) 301.44 ft^2
2) 602.88 cm^2
3) 1413 in^2
4) 401.92 yd^2

Chapter 14: Statistics

Topics that you'll learn in this chapter:

✓ Mean, Median, Mode, and Range of the Given Data

✓ Box and Whisker Plots

✓ Bar Graph

✓ Stem– And– Leaf Plot

✓ The Pie Graph or Circle Graph

✓ Scatter Plots

✓ Probability

Mathematics is no more computation than typing is literature.

– John Allen Paulos

Mean, Median, Mode, and Range of the Given Data

Helpful	- Mean: $\dfrac{\text{sum of the data}}{\text{of data entires}}$	Example:
	- Mode: value in the list that appears most often	22, 16, 12, 9, 7, 6, 4, 6
Hints	- Range: largest value – smallest value	
		Mean = 10.25
		Mod = 6
		Range = 18

✎ *Find Mean, Median, Mode, and Range of the Given Data.*

1) 7, 2, 5, 1, 1, 2

2) 2, 2, 2, 3, 6, 3, 7, 4

3) 9, 4, 3, 1, 7, 9, 4, 6, 4

4) 8, 4, 2, 4, 3, 2, 4, 5

5) 8, 5, 7, 5, 7, 9, 8

6) 5, 1, 4, 4, 9, 2, 9, 2, 5, 1

7) 4, 1, 5, 9, 7, 7, 5, 4, 3, 5

8) 7, 5, 4, 9, 6, 7, 7, 5, 2

9) 2, 5, 5, 6, 2, 4, 7, 6, 4, 9

10) 10, 5, 2, 5, 4, 5, 8, 10

11) 5, 1, 5, 2, 2

12) 2, 3, 5, 9, 6

Bar Graph

Helpful	– A bar graph is a chart that presents data with bars in different heights to match with the values of the data. The bars can be graphed horizontally or vertically.
Hints	

✍️ *Graph the given information as a bar graph.*

Day	Hot dogs sold
Monday	90
Tuesday	70
Wednesday	30
Thursday	20
Friday	60

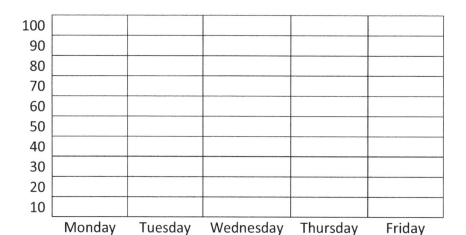

The Pie Graph or Circle Graph

Helpful *Hints*	A Pie Chart is a circle chart divided into sectors, each sector represents the relative size of each value.

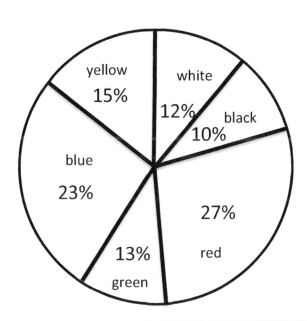

Favorite colors

1) Which color is the most popular?

2) What percentage of pie graph is yellow?

3) Which color is the least popular?

4) What percentage of pie graph is blue?

5) What percentage of pie graph is green?

Scatter Plots

Helpful	A Scatter (xy) Plot shows the values with points that represent the relationship between two sets of data.
Hints	– The horizontal values are usually x and vertical data is y.

✎ *Construct a scatter plot.*

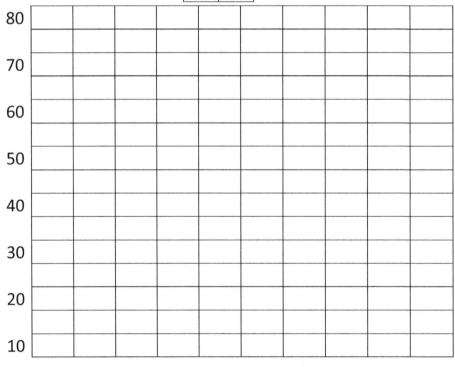

X	Y
1	20
2	40
3	50
4	60

Probability Problems

Helpful Hints	- Probability is the likelihood of something happening in the future. It is expressed as a number between zero (can never happen) to 1 (will always happen). - Probability can be expressed as a fraction, a decimal, or a percent.	Example: Probability of a flipped coins turns up 'heads' Is $0.5 = \dfrac{1}{2}$

✎ **Solve.**

1) A number is chosen at random from 1 to 10. Find the probability of selecting a 4 or smaller.

2) A number is chosen at random from 1 to 50. Find the probability of selecting multiples of 10.

3) A number is chosen at random from 1 to 10. Find the probability of selecting of 4 and factors of 6.

4) A number is chosen at random from 1 to 10. Find the probability of selecting a multiple of 3.

5) A number is chosen at random from 1 to 50. Find the probability of selecting prime numbers.

6) A number is chosen at random from 1 to 25. Find the probability of not selecting a composite number.

Factorials

Helpful	Factorials means to multiply a series of descending natural numbers.	**Example:**
Hints		$4! = 4 \times 3 \times 2 \times 1$

✎ *Determine the value for each expression.*

1) $\dfrac{9!}{6!}$

2) $\dfrac{8!}{5!}$

3) $\dfrac{7!}{5!}$

4) $\dfrac{20!}{18!}$

5) $\dfrac{22!}{18!5!}$

6) $\dfrac{10!}{8!2!}$

7) $\dfrac{100!}{97!}$

8) $\dfrac{14!}{10!4!}$

9) $\dfrac{10!}{8!}$

10) $\dfrac{25!}{20!}$

11) $\dfrac{14!}{9!3!}$

12) $\dfrac{55!}{53!}$

13) $\dfrac{(2.3)!}{3!}$

14) $5! + 4!$

Answers of Worksheets – Chapter 14

Mean, Median, Mode, and Range of the Given Data

1) mean: 3, median: 2, mode: 1, 2, range: 6
2) mean: 3.625, median: 3, mode: 2, range: 5
3) mean: 5.22, median: 4, mode: 4, range: 8
4) mean: 4, median: 4, mode: 4, range: 6
5) mean: 7, median: 7, mode: 5, 7, 8, range: 4
6) mean: 4.2, median: 4, mode: 1,2,4,5,9, range: 8
7) mean: 5, median: 5, mode: 5, range: 8
8) mean: 5.78, median: 6, mode: 7, range: 7
9) mean: 5, median: 5, mode: 2, 4, 5, 6, range: 7
10) mean: 6.125, median: 5, mode: 5, range: 8
11) mean: 3, median: 2, mode: 2, 5, range: 4
12) mean: 5, median: 5, mode: none, range: 7

Bar Graph

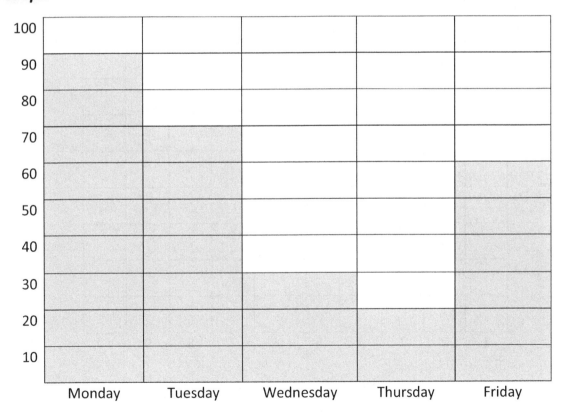

The Pie Graph or Circle Graph

1) red
2) 15%
3) black
4) 23%
5) 13%

Scatter Plots

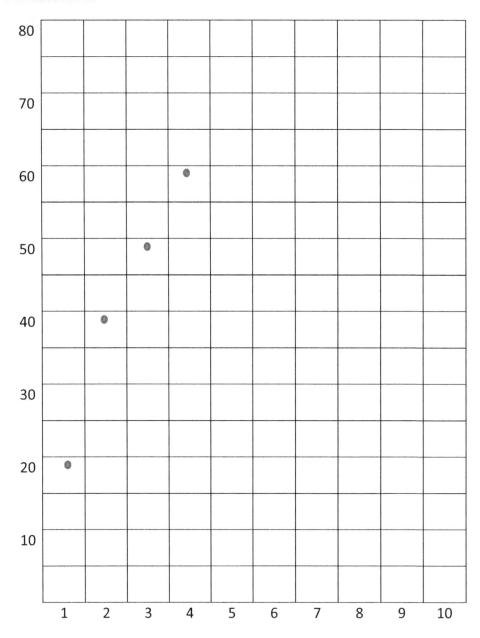

Probability Problems

1) $\frac{2}{5}$

2) $\frac{1}{10}$

3) $\frac{1}{2}$

4) $\frac{3}{10}$

5) $\frac{7}{25}$

6) $\frac{9}{25}$

Factorials

1) 504

2) 336

3) 42

4) 380

5) 1,463

6) 45

7) 970,200

8) 1,001

9) 90

10) 6,375,600

11) 40,040

12) 2,970

13) 120

14) 144

ASTB Test Review

The Aviation Selection Test Battery (known as ASTB), administered at Navy Recruiting Districts (NRDs), is used by the U.S. Navy, Marine Corps, and Coast Guard to select officer aviation program applicants. The newest version of the ASTB is series E. The ASTB-E test is a multiple-aptitude battery that measures developed abilities and helps predict future academic and occupational success in the military. You can only take the ASBT test three times in your lifetime.

The ASTB is a multiple-choice test which consists of 7 subtests.

- Section 1 – Math Skills Test (MST)
- Section 2 – Reading Comprehension Test (RCT)
- Section 3 – Mechanical Comprehension Test (MCT)
- Section 4 – Aviation and Nautical Information Test (ANIT)
- Section 5 – Naval Aviation Trait Facet Inventory (NATFI)
- Section 6 – Performance Based Measures Battery (PBM)
- Section 7 – Biographical Inventory with Response Validation (BI-RV)

The first 5 sections of the ASTB are all computer adaptive. It means that if the correct answer is chosen, the next question will be harder. If the answer given is incorrect, the next question will be easier. This also means that once an answer is selected on the CAT it cannot be changed.

The Mathematics section of ASTB contains 20 to 30 multiple-choice questions assess content in the following areas:

- Number Sense and Operations
- Algebra
- Data, Statistics, And Probability
- Geometry and Measurement

You have 40 minutes to complete the first (Math) section of the test. The ASTB test does not allow you to use a calculator, but a few formulas are provided for some questions.

In this book, there are two complete ASTB-E Mathematics Tests. Take these tests to see what score you'll be able to receive on a real ASTB test.

Good luck!

Time to Test

Time to refine your math skill with a practice test

Take an ASTB-E Math test to simulate the test day experience. After you've finished, score your test using the answer keys.

Before You Start

- You'll need a pencil, a calculator and a timer to take the test.

- For each question, there are five possible answers. Choose which one is best.

- It's okay to guess. There is no penalty for wrong answers.

- Use the answer sheet provided to record your answers.

- You have 40 minutes to complete each test. Answer as many questions as possible.

- After you've finished the test, review the answer key to see where you went wrong.

Good Luck!

ASBT Math
Practice Test 1

2020 - 2021

Total number of questions: 30

Total time: 40 Minutes

On a real ASTB test, Math Formulas are provided for some questions.

You may NOT use a calculator on this practice test.

ASTB Math Practice Tests Answer Sheet

Remove (or photocopy) this answer sheet and use it to complete the practice tests.

ASBT Math Practice Test Answer Sheet

1	Ⓐ Ⓑ Ⓒ Ⓓ	16	Ⓐ Ⓑ Ⓒ Ⓓ
2	Ⓐ Ⓑ Ⓒ Ⓓ	17	Ⓐ Ⓑ Ⓒ Ⓓ
3	Ⓐ Ⓑ Ⓒ Ⓓ	18	Ⓐ Ⓑ Ⓒ Ⓓ
4	Ⓐ Ⓑ Ⓒ Ⓓ	19	Ⓐ Ⓑ Ⓒ Ⓓ
5	Ⓐ Ⓑ Ⓒ Ⓓ	20	Ⓐ Ⓑ Ⓒ Ⓓ
6	Ⓐ Ⓑ Ⓒ Ⓓ	21	Ⓐ Ⓑ Ⓒ Ⓓ
7	Ⓐ Ⓑ Ⓒ Ⓓ	22	Ⓐ Ⓑ Ⓒ Ⓓ
8	Ⓐ Ⓑ Ⓒ Ⓓ	23	Ⓐ Ⓑ Ⓒ Ⓓ
9	Ⓐ Ⓑ Ⓒ Ⓓ	24	Ⓐ Ⓑ Ⓒ Ⓓ
10	Ⓐ Ⓑ Ⓒ Ⓓ	25	Ⓐ Ⓑ Ⓒ Ⓓ
11	Ⓐ Ⓑ Ⓒ Ⓓ	26	Ⓐ Ⓑ Ⓒ Ⓓ
12	Ⓐ Ⓑ Ⓒ Ⓓ	27	Ⓐ Ⓑ Ⓒ Ⓓ
13	Ⓐ Ⓑ Ⓒ Ⓓ	28	Ⓐ Ⓑ Ⓒ Ⓓ
14	Ⓐ Ⓑ Ⓒ Ⓓ	29	Ⓐ Ⓑ Ⓒ Ⓓ
15	Ⓐ Ⓑ Ⓒ Ⓓ	30	Ⓐ Ⓑ Ⓒ Ⓓ

ASBT Math Practice Test

ASTB Mathematics Formula Sheet

Area of a:

Triangle $\qquad A = \dfrac{1}{2}bh$

Parallelogram $\qquad A = bh$

Trapezoid $\qquad A = \dfrac{1}{2}h\,(b_1 + b_2)$

Circle $\qquad A = \pi r^2$

Volume of a:

Rectangular/Right Prism $\qquad V = Bh$

Cylinder $\qquad V = \pi r^2 h$

Algebra

Slope of a line $\qquad m = \dfrac{y_2 - y_1}{x_2 - x_1}$

The equation of a line $\qquad y = mx + b$

Pythagorean theorem $\qquad a^2 + b^2 = c^2$

Simple interest $\qquad I = prt$

(I = interest, p = principal, r = rate, t = time)

Length

Customary	**Metric**
1 mile = 1,760 yards (yd)	1 kilometer (km) = 1,000 meter (m)
1 yard = 3 feet (ft)	1 meter (m) = 100 centimeters (cm)
1 foot (ft) = 12 inches (in.)	1 centimeter (cm) = 10 millimeters (mm)

Volume and Capacity

Customary	**Metric**
1 gallon (gal) = 4 quarts (qt)	1 liter (L) = 1,000 millimeters (mL)
1 quart (qt) = 2 pints (pt)	
1 pint (pt) = 2 cups (c)	
1 cup (c) = 8 fluid ounces (fl oz)	

1) The mean of 50 test scores was calculated as 90. But, it turned out that one of the scores was misread as 94 but it was 69. What is the mean?
   A. 85
   B. 87
   C. 89.5
   D. 90.5

2) Two dice are thrown simultaneously, what is the probability of getting a sum of 5 or 8?
   A. $\dfrac{1}{3}$
   B. $\dfrac{11}{36}$
   C. $\dfrac{1}{16}$
   D. $\dfrac{1}{4}$

3) Which of the following is equal to the expression below?

$$(5x + 2y)(2x - y)$$

   A. $4x^2 - 2y^2$
   B. $2x^2 + 6xy - 2y^2$
   C. $24x^2 + 2xy - 2y^2$
   D. $10x^2 - xy - 2y^2$

4) What is the product of all possible values of x in the following equation?

$$|x - 10| = 4$$

   A. 3
   B. 7
   C. 13
   D. 84

5) What is the slope of a line that is perpendicular to the line
$$4x - 2y = 6?$$
   A. -2
   B. $-\dfrac{1}{2}$
   C. 4
   D. 12

6) What is the value of the expression $6(x - 2y) + (2 - x)^2$ when $x = 3$ and $y = -2$?
   A. -4
   B. 20
   C. 43
   D. 50

7) A swimming pool holds 2,500 cubic feet of water. The swimming pool is 25 feet long and 10 feet wide. How deep is the swimming pool?
   A. $2\ feet$
   B. $4\ feet$
   C. $6\ feet$
   D. $10\ feet$

8) Four one – foot rulers can be split among how many users to leave each with $\frac{1}{3}$ of a ruler?
   A. 4
   B. 6
   C. 12
   D. 24

9) What is the area of a square whose diagonal is 4?
   A. 4
   B. 8
   C. 16
   D. 64

10) The average of five numbers is 26. If a sixth number 42 is added, then, what is the new average? (round your answer to the nearest hundredth)
    A. 25
    B. 26.5
    C. 27
    D. 28.66

11) The ratio of boys and girls in a class is $4:7$. If there are 55 students in the class, how many more boys should be enrolled to make the ratio $1:1$?
    A. 8
    B. 10
    C. 15
    D. 20

12) Mr. Jones saves $2,500 out of his monthly family income of $65,000. What fractional part of his income does he save?

   A. $\frac{1}{26}$

   B. $\frac{1}{11}$

   C. $\frac{3}{25}$

   D. $\frac{2}{15}$

13) A football team had $20,000 to spend on supplies. The team spent $14,000 on new balls. New sport shoes cost $110 each. Which of the following inequalities represent how many new shoes the team can purchase.

   A. $110x + 14,000 \le 20,000$

   B. $110x + 14,000 \ge 20,000$

   C. $14,000x + 110 \le 20,000$

   D. $14,000x + 110 \ge 20,000$

14) Jason needs an 70% average in his writing class to pass. On his first 4 exams, he earned scores of 68%, 72%, 85%, and 90%. What is the minimum score Jason can earn on his fifth and final test to pass?

   A. 80%,

   B. 70%

   C. 68%

   D. 35%

15) What is the value of x in the following equation? $\frac{2}{3}x + \frac{1}{6} = \frac{1}{2}$

   A. 6

   B. $\frac{1}{2}$

   C. $\frac{1}{3}$

   D. $\frac{1}{4}$

16) A bank is offering 4.5% simple interest on a savings account. If you deposit $12,000, how much interest will you earn in two years?

   A. $420

   B. $1,080

   C. $4,200

   D. $8,400

17) Simplify $7x^2y^3(2x^2y)^3 =$

A. $12x^4y^6$
B. $12x^8y^6$
C. $56x^4y^6$
D. $56x^8y^6$

18) What is the surface area of the cylinder below?

A. $40\,\pi\ in^2$
B. $57\,\pi\ in^2$
C. $66\,\pi\ in^2$
D. $288\,\pi\ in^2$

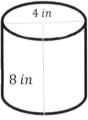

4 in

8 in

19) Last week 25,000 fans attended a football match. This week three times as many bought tickets, but one sixth of them cancelled their tickets. How many are attending this week?
A. 48,000
B. 54,000
C. 62,500
D. 75,000

20) What is the perimeter of a square that has an area of 49 square inches?
A. 144 *inches*
B. 64 *inches*
C. 56 *inches*
D. 28 *inches*

21) If the ratio of $5a$ to $2b$ is $\frac{1}{10}$, what is the ratio of a to b?

A. 10

B. 25

C. $\frac{1}{25}$

D. $\frac{1}{20}$

22) A cruise line ship left Port A and traveled 50 miles due west and then 120 miles due north. At this point, what is the shortest distance from the cruise to port A?
A. 70 *miles*
B. 80 *miles*
C. 150 *miles*
D. 130 *miles*

23) What is the equivalent temperature of $104°F$ in Celsius?

$$C = \frac{5}{9}(F - 32)$$

   A. 32
   B. 40
   C. 48
   D. 52

24) The perimeter of a rectangular yard is 72 meters. What is its length if its width is twice its length?
   A. 12 *meters*
   B. 18 *meters*
   C. 20 *meters*
   D. 24 *meters*

25) The average of 6 numbers is 14. The average of 4 of those numbers is 10. What is the average of the other two numbers?
   A. 10
   B. 12
   C. 14
   D. 22

26) If 150% of a number is 75, then what is the 80% of that number?
   A. 40
   B. 50
   C. 70
   D. 85

27) What is the slope of the line: $4x - 2y = 12$
   A. -1
   B. -2
   C. 1
   D. 2

28) In two successive years, the population of a town is increased by 10% and 20%. What percent of the population is increased after two years?
   A. 30%
   B. 32%
   C. 35%
   D. 68%

29) The area of a circle is 36π. What is the diameter of the circle?

    A. 4
    B. 8
    C. 12
    D. 14

30) If 20% of a number is 4, what is the number?

    A. 4
    B. 8
    C. 10
    D. 20

End of ASTB Math Practice Test

ASBT Math
Practice Test 2
2020 - 2021

Total number of questions: 30

Total time: 40 Minutes

On a real ASTB test, Math Formulas are provided for some questions.

You may NOT use a calculator on this practice test.

ASTB Math Practice Tests Answer Sheet

Remove (or photocopy) this answer sheet and use it to complete the practice tests.

ASBT Math Practice Test Answer Sheet

ASBT Math Practice Test

1	Ⓐ Ⓑ Ⓒ Ⓓ	16	Ⓐ Ⓑ Ⓒ Ⓓ
2	Ⓐ Ⓑ Ⓒ Ⓓ	17	Ⓐ Ⓑ Ⓒ Ⓓ
3	Ⓐ Ⓑ Ⓒ Ⓓ	18	Ⓐ Ⓑ Ⓒ Ⓓ
4	Ⓐ Ⓑ Ⓒ Ⓓ	19	Ⓐ Ⓑ Ⓒ Ⓓ
5	Ⓐ Ⓑ Ⓒ Ⓓ	20	Ⓐ Ⓑ Ⓒ Ⓓ
6	Ⓐ Ⓑ Ⓒ Ⓓ	21	Ⓐ Ⓑ Ⓒ Ⓓ
7	Ⓐ Ⓑ Ⓒ Ⓓ	22	Ⓐ Ⓑ Ⓒ Ⓓ
8	Ⓐ Ⓑ Ⓒ Ⓓ	23	Ⓐ Ⓑ Ⓒ Ⓓ
9	Ⓐ Ⓑ Ⓒ Ⓓ	24	Ⓐ Ⓑ Ⓒ Ⓓ
10	Ⓐ Ⓑ Ⓒ Ⓓ	25	Ⓐ Ⓑ Ⓒ Ⓓ
11	Ⓐ Ⓑ Ⓒ Ⓓ	26	Ⓐ Ⓑ Ⓒ Ⓓ
12	Ⓐ Ⓑ Ⓒ Ⓓ	27	Ⓐ Ⓑ Ⓒ Ⓓ
13	Ⓐ Ⓑ Ⓒ Ⓓ	28	Ⓐ Ⓑ Ⓒ Ⓓ
14	Ⓐ Ⓑ Ⓒ Ⓓ	29	Ⓐ Ⓑ Ⓒ Ⓓ
15	Ⓐ Ⓑ Ⓒ Ⓓ	30	Ⓐ Ⓑ Ⓒ Ⓓ

ASTB Mathematics Formula Sheet

Area of a:

Triangle $\qquad\qquad\qquad\qquad A = \dfrac{1}{2}bh$

Parallelogram $\qquad\qquad\quad A = bh$

Trapezoid $\qquad\qquad\qquad\; A = \dfrac{1}{2}h\,(b_1 + b_2)$

Circle $\qquad\qquad\qquad\qquad A = \pi r^2$

Volume of a:

Rectangular/Right Prism

$\qquad\qquad\qquad\qquad\qquad V = Bh$

Cylinder $\qquad\qquad\qquad\quad V = \pi r^2 h$

Algebra

Slope of a line $\qquad\qquad\quad m = \dfrac{y_2 - y_1}{x_2 - x_1}$

The equation of a line $\qquad y = mx + b$

Pythagorean theorem $\qquad a^2 + b^2 = c^2$

Simple interest $\qquad\qquad\qquad\qquad I = prt$

$(I$ = interest, p = principal, r = rate, t = time$)$

Length

Customary	**Metric**
1 mile = 1,760 yards (yd)	1 kilometer (km) = 1,000 meter (m)
1 yard = 3 feet (ft)	1 meter (m) = 100 centimeters (cm)
1 foot (ft) = 12 inches (in.)	1 centimeter (cm) = 10 millimeters (mm)

Volume and Capacity

Customary	**Metric**
1 gallon (gal) = 4 quarts (qt)	1 liter (L) = 1,000 millimeters (mL)
1 quart (qt) = 2 pints (pt)	
1 pint (pt) = 2 cups (c)	
1 cup (c) = 8 fluid ounces (fl oz)	

1) When a number is subtracted from 24 and the difference is divided by that number, the result is 3. What is the value of the number?
   A. 2
   B. 4
   C. 6
   D. 12

2) An angle is equal to one fifth of its supplement. What is the measure of that angle?
   A. 20
   B. 30
   C. 45
   D. 60

3) John traveled 150 km in 6 hours and Alice traveled 180 km in 4 hours. What is the ratio of the average speed of John to average speed of Alice?
   A. 3 : 2
   B. 2 : 3
   C. 5 : 9
   D. 5 : 6

4) If 40% of a class are girls, and 35% of girls play tennis, what percent of the class play tennis?
   A. 10%
   B. 14%
   C. 20%
   D. 40%

5) In five successive hours, a car traveled 40 km, 45 km, 50 km, 35 km and 55 km. In the next five hours, it traveled with an average speed of 50 $km\ per\ hour$. Find the total distance the car traveled in 10 hours.
   A. 425 km
   B. 450 km
   C. 475 km
   D. 500 km

6) How long does a 420–miles trip take moving at 50 miles per hour (mph)?
   A. 4 $hours$
   B. 6 $hours\ and\ 24\ minutes$
   C. 8 $hours\ and\ 24\ minutes$
   D. 8 $hours\ and\ 30\ minutes$

7) Right triangle ABC has two legs of lengths $6\ cm\ (AB)$ and $8\ cm\ (AC)$. What is the length of the third side (BC)?
   A. $4\ cm$
   B. $6\ cm$
   C. $8\ cm$
   D. $10\ cm$

8) The ratio of boys to girls in a school is $2:3$. If there are 600 students in a school, how many boys are in the school.
   A. 540
   B. 360
   C. 300
   D. 240

9) 25 is What percent of 20?
   A. 20%
   B. 25%
   C. 125%
   D. 150%

10) The perimeter of the trapezoid below is 54. What is its area?
   A. $252\ cm^2$
   B. $234\ cm^2$
   C. $216\ cm^2$
   D. $130\ cm^2$

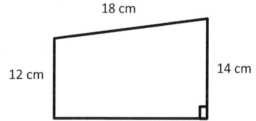

11) Two third of 18 is equal to $\frac{2}{5}$ of what number?
   A. 12
   B. 20
   C. 30
   D. 60

12) The marked price of a computer is D dollar. Its price decreased by 20% in January and later increased by 10% in February. What is the final price of the computer in D dollar?
   A. $0.80\ D$
   B. $0.88\ D$
   C. $0.90\ D$
   D. $1.20\ D$

13) The area of a circle is $25\,\pi$. What is the circumference of the circle?

   A. $5\,\pi$
   B. $10\,\pi$
   C. $32\,\pi$
   D. $64\,\pi$

14) In 1999, the average worker's income increased \$3,000 per year starting from \$24,000 annual salary. Which equation represents income greater than average? (I = income, x = number of years after 1999)

   A. $I > 3000\,x + 24000$
   B. $I > -3000\,x + 24000$
   C. $I < -3000\,x + 24000$
   D. $I < 3000\,x - 24000$

15) From last year, the price of gasoline has increased from \$1.25 per gallon to \$1.75 per gallon. The new price is what percent of the original price?

   A. 72%
   B. 120%
   C. 140%
   D. 160%

16) A boat sails 40 miles south and then 30 miles east. How far is the boat from its start point?

   A. $45\ miles$
   B. $50\ miles$
   C. $60\ miles$
   D. $70\ miles$

17) If $x = 9$, what is the value of y in the following equation?

$$2y = \frac{2x^2}{3} + 6$$

   A. 30
   B. 45
   C. 60
   D. 120

18) The score of Emma was half as that of Ava and the score of Mia was twice that of Ava. If the score of Mia was 60, what is the score of Emma?
   A. 12
   B. 15
   C. 20
   D. 30

19) The average of five consecutive numbers is 38. What is the smallest number?
   A. 38
   B. 36
   C. 34
   D. 12

20) How many tiles of $8\ cm^2$ is needed to cover a floor of dimension $6\ cm$ by $24\ cm$?
   A. 6
   B. 12
   C. 18
   D. 24

21) A rope weighs 600 grams per meter of length. What is the weight in kilograms of 12.2 meters of this rope? ($1\ kilograms\ =\ 1000\ grams$)
   A. 0.0732
   B. 0.732
   C. 7.32
   D. 7,320

22) A chemical solution contains 4% alcohol. If there is $24\ ml$ of alcohol, what is the volume of the solution?
   A. $240\ ml$
   B. $480\ ml$
   C. $600\ ml$
   D. $1,200\ ml$

23) The average weight of 18 girls in a class is $60\ kg$ and the average weight of 32 boys in the same class is $62\ kg$. What is the average weight of all the 50 students in that class?
   A. 60
   B. 61.28
   C. 61.68
   D. 61.90

24) The price of a laptop is decreased by 10% to $360. What is its original price?
    A. $320
    B. $380
    C. $400
    D. $450

25) The radius of a cylinder is 8 inches and its height is 12 inches. What is the surface area of the cylinder?
    A. $64\,\pi\ in^2$
    B. $128\,\pi\ in^2$
    C. $192\,\pi\ in^2$
    D. $320\,\pi\ in^2$

26) The average of $13, 15, 20$ and x is 18. What is the value of x?
    A. 9
    B. 15
    C. 18
    D. 24

27) The price of a sofa is decreased by 25% to $420. What was its original price?
    A. $480
    B. $520
    C. $560
    D. $600

28) A bank is offering 4.5% simple interest on a savings account. If you deposit $8,000, how much interest will you earn in five years?
    A. $360
    B. $720
    C. $1,800
    D. $3,600

29) Multiply and write the product in scientific notation:

$$(4.2 \times 10^6) \times (2.6 \times 10^{-5})$$

    A. 1092×10
    B. 10.92×10^6
    C. 109.2×10^{-5}
    D. 1.092×10^2

30) If the height of a right pyramid is $12\ cm$ and its base is a square with side $6\ cm$. What is its volume?

    A. $32\ cm^3$

    B. $36\ cm^3$

    C. $48\ cm^3$

    D. $144\ cm^3$

End of ASTB Math Practice Test

ASTB Math Practice Tests
Answer Keys

Now, it's time to review your results to see where you went wrong and what areas you need to improve.

ASTB Math Practice Test 1				ASTB Math Practice Test 2			
1	C	21	C	1	C	21	C
2	D	22	D	2	B	22	C
3	D	23	B	3	C	23	B
4	D	24	A	4	B	24	C
5	B	25	D	5	C	25	D
6	C	26	A	6	C	26	D
7	D	27	D	7	D	27	C
8	C	28	B	8	D	28	C
9	B	29	C	9	C	29	D
10	D	30	D	10	D	30	D
11	C			11	C		
12	A			12	B		
13	A			13	B		
14	D			14	A		
15	B			15	C		
16	B			16	B		
17	D			17	A		
18	A			18	B		
19	C			19	B		
20	D			20	C		

ASTB Math Practice Tests
Answers and Explanations

ASTB Math Practice Test 1

1) Choice C is correct

$$average\ (mean) = \frac{sum\ of\ terms}{number\ of\ terms} \Rightarrow 90 = \frac{sum\ of\ terms}{50} \Rightarrow sum = 90 \times 50 = 4500$$

The difference of 94 and 69 is 25. Therefore, 25 should be subtracted from the sum.

$$4500 - 25 = 4475, mean = \frac{sum\ of\ terms}{number\ of\ terms} \Rightarrow mean = \frac{4475}{50} = 89.5$$

2) Choice D is correct

For sum of 5: $(1\ \&\ 4)$ and $(4\ \&\ 1), (2\ \&\ 3)$ and $(3\ \&\ 2)$, therefore we have 4 options.
For sum of 8: $(5\ \&\ 3)$ and $(3\ \&\ 5), (4\ \&\ 4)$ and $(2\ \&\ 6)$, and $(6\ \&\ 2)$, we have 5 options. To get a sum of 5 or 8 for two dice: $4 + 5 = 9$. Since, we have $6 \times 6 = 36$ total number of options, the probability of getting a sum of 5 and 8 is 9 out of 36 or $\frac{9}{36} = \frac{1}{4}$.

3) Choice D is correct

Use FOIL method. $(5x + 2y)(2x - y) = 10x^2 - 5xy + 4xy - 2y^2 = 10x^2 - xy - 2y^2$

4) Choice D is correct

To solve absolute values equations, write two equations. $x - 10$ could be positive 4, or negative 4. Therefore, $x - 10 = 4 \Rightarrow x = 14$, $x - 10 = -4 \Rightarrow x = 6$. Find the product of solutions: $6 \times 14 = 84$

5) Choice B is correct

The equation of a line in slope intercept form is: $y = \mathrm{m}x + b$. Solve for y.

$4x - 2y = 6 \Rightarrow -2y = 6 - 4x \Rightarrow y = (6 - 4x) \div (-2) \Rightarrow y = 2x - 3$. The slope is 2.

The slope of the line perpendicular to this line is: $m_1 \times m_2 = -1 \Rightarrow 2 \times m_2 = -1 \Rightarrow m_2 = -\frac{1}{2}$.

6) Choice C is correct

Plug in the value of x and y. $x = 3$ and $y = -2$.

$6(x - 2y) + (2 - x)^2 = 6(3 - 2(-2)) + (2 - 3)^2 = 6(3 + 4) + (-1)^2 = 42 + 1 = 43$

7) Choice D is correct

Use formula of rectangle prism volume.$V = (length)\ (width)\ (height) \Rightarrow 2500 = (25)\ (10)\ (height) \Rightarrow height = 2500 \div 250 = 10$

8) Choice C is correct

$$4 \div \frac{1}{3} = 12$$

9) Choice B is correct

The diagonal of the square is 4. Let x be the side. Use Pythagorean Theorem: $a^2 + b^2 = c^2$

$$x^2 + x^2 = 4^2 \Rightarrow 2x^2 = 4^2 \Rightarrow 2x^2 = 16 \Rightarrow x^2 = 8 \Rightarrow x = \sqrt{8}$$

The area of the square is: $\sqrt{8} \times \sqrt{8} = 8$

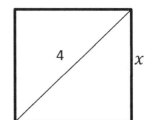

10) Choice D is correct

Solve for the sum of five numbers.

$$average = \frac{\text{sum of terms}}{\text{number of terms}} \Rightarrow 26 = \frac{sum\ of\ 5\ numbers}{5} \Rightarrow sum\ of\ 5\ numbers = 26 \times 5 = 130$$

The sum of 5 numbers is 130. If a sixth number 42 is added, then the sum of 6 numbers is

$$130 + 42 = 172.\ average = \frac{\text{sum of terms}}{\text{number of terms}} = \frac{172}{6} = 28.66$$

11) Choice C is correct

Th ratio of boy to girls is $4 : 7$. Therefore, there are 4 boys out of 11 students. To find the answer, first divide the total number of students by 11, then multiply the result by 4.

$55 \div 11 = 5 \Rightarrow 5 \times 4 = 20$. There are 20 boys and 35 $(55 - 20)$ girls. So, 15 more boys should be enrolled to make the ratio $1 : 1$

12) Choice A is correct

2,500 out of 65,000 equals to $\frac{2500}{65000} = \frac{25}{650} = \frac{1}{26}$

13) Choice A is correct

Let x be the number of shoes the team can purchase. Therefore, the team can purchase $110\ x$.

The team had $20,000 and spent $14000. Now the team can spend on new shoes $6000 at most. Now, write the inequality: $110x + 14,000 \leq 20,000$

14) Choice D is correct

Jason needs an 70% average to pass for five exams. Therefore, the sum of 5 exams must be at lease $5 \times 70 = 350$. The sum of 4 exams is: $68 + 72 + 85 + 90 = 315$.

The minimum score Jason can earn on his fifth and final test to pass is: $350 - 315 = 35$

15) Choice B is correct

Isolate and solve for $x.\frac{2}{3}x + \frac{1}{6} = \frac{1}{2} \Rightarrow \frac{2}{3}x = \frac{1}{2} - \frac{1}{6} = \frac{1}{3} \Rightarrow \frac{2}{3}x = \frac{1}{3}$ .Multiply both sides by the reciprocal of the coefficient of x. $(\frac{3}{2})\frac{1}{3}x = \frac{1}{3}(\frac{3}{2}) \Rightarrow x = \frac{3}{6} = \frac{1}{2}$

16) Choice B is correct

Use simple interest formula: $I = prt$ ($I =$ interest, $p =$ principal, $r =$ rate, $t =$ time).

$$I = (12,000)(0.045)(2) = 1,080$$

17) Choice D is correct

Simplify. $7x^2y^3(2x^2y)^3 = 7x^2y^3(8x^6y^3) = 56x^8y^6$

18) Choice A is correct

Surface Area of a cylinder $= 2\pi r (r + h)$, The radius of the cylinder is $2 (4 \div 2)$ inches and its height is 8 inches. Therefore, Surface Area of a cylinder $= 2\pi (2) (2 + 8) = 40\pi$

19) Choice C is correct

Three times of 25,000 is 75,000. One sixth of them cancelled their tickets. One sixth of 75,000 equals 12,500 ($\frac{1}{6} \times 75000 = 12500$). 62,500 ($75000 - 12000 = 62500$) fans are attending this week.

20) Choice D is correct

The area of the square is 49 inches. Therefore, the side of the square is square root of the area.

$\sqrt{49} = 7$ inches. Four times the side of the square is the perimeter: $4 \times 7 = 28\ inches$

21) Choice C is correct

Write the ratio of $5a$ to $2b$. $\frac{5a}{2b} = \frac{1}{10}$. Use cross multiplication and then simplify.

$$5a \times 10 = 2b \times 1 \rightarrow 50a = 2b \rightarrow a = \frac{2b}{50} = \frac{b}{25}$$

Now, find the ratio of a to b. $\frac{a}{b} = \frac{\frac{b}{25}}{b} \rightarrow \frac{b}{25} \div b = \frac{b}{25} \times \frac{1}{b} = \frac{b}{25} = \frac{1}{25}$

22) Choice D is correct

Use the information provided in the question to draw the shape.

Use Pythagorean Theorem: $a^2 + b^2 = c^2$

$50^2 + 120^2 = c^2 \Rightarrow 2{,}500 + 14{,}400 = c^2 \Rightarrow 16{,}900 = c^2 \Rightarrow c = 130$

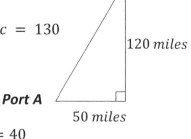

Port A

120 *miles*

50 *miles*

23) Choice B is correct

Plug in 104 for F and then solve for C.

$$C = \frac{5}{9}(F - 32) \Rightarrow C = \frac{5}{9}(104 - 32) \Rightarrow C = \frac{5}{9}(72) = 40$$

24) Choice A is correct

The width of the rectangle is twice its length. Let x be the length. Then, $width = 2x$

Perimeter of the rectangle is $2\,(width + length) = 2(2x + x) = 72 \Rightarrow 6x = 72 \Rightarrow x = 12$. Length of the rectangle is 12 meters.

25) Choice D is correct

$average = \frac{\text{sum of terms}}{\text{number of terms}} \Rightarrow$ (average of 6 numbers) $14 = \frac{\text{sum of numbers}}{6} \Rightarrow$ sum of 6 numbers is $14 \times 6 = 84$, (average of 4 numbers) $10 = \frac{\text{sum of numbers}}{4} \Rightarrow$ sum of 4 numbers is $10 \times 4 = 40$. *sum of 6 numbers* $-$ *sum of 4 numbers* $=$ *sum of 2 numbers*,

$84 - 40 = 44$ average of 2 numbers $= \frac{44}{2} = 22$

26) Choice A is correct

First, find the number. Let x be the number. Write the equation and solve for x. 150% of a number is 75, then:$1.5 \times x = 75 \Rightarrow x = 75 \div 1.5 = 50$, 80% of 50 is:$0.8 \times 50 = 40$

27) Choice D is correct

Solve for $y.4x - 2y = 12 \Rightarrow -2y = 12 - 4x \Rightarrow y = 2x - 6$. The slope of the line is 2.

28) Choice B is correct

the population is increased by 10% and 20%. 10% increase changes the population to 110% of original population. For the second increase, multiply the result by 120%.

$(1.10) \times (1.20) = 1.32 = 132\%$. 32 percent of the population is increased after two years.

29) Choice C is correct

The formula for the area of the circle is: $A = \pi r^2$,The area is 36π. Therefore:$A = \pi r^2 \Rightarrow 6\pi = \pi r^2$, Divide both sides by π: $36 = r^2 \Rightarrow \boldsymbol{r = 6}$. Diameter of a circle is $2 \times$ radius. Then:

$Diameter = 2 \times 6 = 12$

30) Choice D is correct

If 20% of a number is 4, what is the number: $20\% \ of \ x = 4 \Rightarrow 0.20 \ x = 4 \Rightarrow x = 4 \div 0.20 = 20$

ASTB Math Practice Test 2

1) Choice C is correct

Let x be the number. Write the equation and solve for x. $(24 - x) \div x = 3$. Multiply both sides by x. $(24 - x) = 3x$, then add x both sides. $24 = 4x$, now divide both sides by 4.

$x = 6$

2) Choice B is correct

The sum of supplement angles is 180. Let x be that angle. Therefore, $x + 5x = 180$

$6x = 180$, divide both sides by 6: $x = 30$

3) Choice C is correct

The average speed of john is: $150 \div 6 = 25$, The average speed of Alice is: $180 \div 4 = 45$

Write the ratio and simplify. $25 : 45 \Rightarrow 5 : 9$

4) Choice B is correct

The percent of girls playing tennis is: $40\% \times 35\% = 0.40 \times 0.35 = 0.14 = 14\%$

5) Choice C is correct

Add the first 5 numbers. $40 + 45 + 50 + 35 + 55 = 225$

To find the distance traveled in the next 5 hours, multiply the average by number of hours.

$Distance = Average \times Rate = 50 \times 5 = 250$, Add both numbers. $250 + 225 = 475$

6) Choice C is correct

Use distance formula: $Distance = Rate \times time \Rightarrow 420 = 50 \times T$, divide both sides by 50. $420 \div 50 = T \Rightarrow T = 8.4 \ hours$. Change hours to minutes for the decimal part. $0.4 \ hours = 0.4 \times 60 = 24 \ minutes$.

7) Choice D is correct

Use Pythagorean Theorem: $a^2 + b^2 = c^2$, $6^2 + 8^2 = c^2 \Rightarrow 100 = c^2 \Rightarrow c = 10$

8) Choice D is correct

Th ratio of boy to girls is $2:3$. Therefore, there are 2 boys out of 5 students. To find the answer, first divide the total number of students by 5, then multiply the result by 2.

$600 \div 5 = 120 \Rightarrow 120 \times 2 = 240$

9) Choice C is correct

Use percent formula: $part = \frac{percent}{100} \times whole$

$$25 = \frac{percent}{100} \times 20 \Rightarrow 25 = \frac{percent \times 20}{100} \Rightarrow 25$$
$$= \frac{percent \times 2}{10}, multiply\ both\ sides\ by\ 10.$$
$250 = percent \times 2$, divide both sides by 2. $125 = percent$

10) Choice D is correct

The perimeter of the trapezoid is 54.

Therefore, the missing side (height) is $= 54 - 18 - 12 - 14 = 10$

Area of the trapezoid: $A = \frac{1}{2}h(b_1 + b_2) = \frac{1}{2}(10)(12 + 14) = 130$

11) Choice C is correct

Let x be the number. Write the equation and solve for x.

$\frac{2}{3} \times 18 = \frac{2}{5} \cdot x \Rightarrow \frac{2 \times 18}{3} = \frac{2x}{5}$, use cross multiplication to solve for x.

$5 \times 36 = 2x \times 3 \Rightarrow 180 = 6x \Rightarrow x = 30$

12) Choice B is correct

To find the discount, multiply the number by $(100\% - rate\ of\ discount)$.

Therefore, for the first discount we get: $(D)(100\% - 20\%) = (D)(0.80) = 0.80\,D$

For increase of 10%: $(0.80\,D)(100\% + 10\%) = (0.80\,D)(1.10) = 0.88\,D = 88\%\ of\ D$

13) Choice B is correct

Use the formula of areas of circles. $Area = \pi r^2 \Rightarrow 25\pi = \pi r^2 \Rightarrow 25 = r^2 \Rightarrow r = 5$

Radius of the circle is 5. Now, use the circumference formula: Circumference $= 2\pi r = 2\pi(5) = 10\pi$

14) Choice A is correct

Let x be the number of years. Therefore, \$3,000 per year equals $2000x$. starting from \$24,000 annual salary means you should add that amount to $3000x$. Income more than that is:

$$I > 3000\,x + 24000$$

15) Choice C is correct

The question is this: 1.75 is what percent of 1.25? Use percent formula:

$$\text{part} = \frac{\text{percent}}{100} \times \text{whole}$$
$$1.75 = \frac{percent}{100} \times 1.25 \Rightarrow 1.75 = \frac{percent \times 1.25}{100} \Rightarrow 175 = percent \times 1.25$$
$$\Rightarrow percent = \frac{175}{1.25} = 140$$

16) Choice B is correct

Use the information provided in the question to draw the shape.

Use Pythagorean Theorem: $a^2 + b^2 = c^2$

$$40^2 + 30^2 = c^2 \Rightarrow 1600 + 900 = c^2 \Rightarrow 2500 = c^2 \Rightarrow c = 50$$

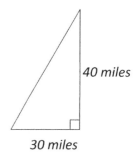

40 miles

30 miles

17) Choice A is correct

Plug in the value of x in the equation and solve for y. $2y = \frac{2x^2}{3} + 6 \rightarrow 2y = \frac{2(9)^2}{3} + 6 \rightarrow$

$$2y = \frac{2(81)}{3} + 6 \rightarrow 2y = 54 + 6 = 60 \rightarrow 2y = 60 \rightarrow y = 30$$

18) Choice B is correct

If the score of Mia was 60, therefore the score of Ava is 30. Since, the score of Emma was half as that of Ava, therefore, the score of Emma is 15.

19) Choice B is correct

Let x be the smallest number. Then, these are the numbers:$x, x + 1, x + 2, x + 3, x + 4$

$average = \frac{\text{sum of terms}}{\text{number of terms}} \Rightarrow 38 = \frac{x+(x+1)+(x+2)+(x+3)+(x+4)}{5} \Rightarrow 38 = \frac{5x+10}{5} \Rightarrow 190 = 5x + 10 \Rightarrow 180 = 5x \Rightarrow x = 36$

20) Choice C is correct

The area of the floor is: $6\ cm \times 24\ cm = 144\ cm^2$, The number is tiles needed $= 144 \div 8 = 18$

21) Choice C is correct

The weight of 12.2 meters of this rope is: $12.2 \times 600\ g = 7320\ g$,

$1\ kg = 1000\ g$, therefore, $7320\ g \div 1000 = 7.32\ kg$

22) Choice C is correct

4% of the volume of the solution is alcohol. Let x be the volume of the solution.

Then: $4\%\ of\ x = 24\ ml \Rightarrow 0.04\ x = 24 \Rightarrow x = 24 \div 0.04 = 600$

23) Choice B is correct

$average = \frac{sum\ of\ terms}{number\ of\ terms}$, The sum of the weight of all girls is: $18 \times 60 = 1080\ kg$, The sum of the weight of all boys is: $32 \times 62 = 1984\ kg$, The sum of the weight of all students is: $1080 + 1984 = 3064\ kg$, average $= \frac{3064}{50} = 61.28$

24) Choice C is correct

Let x be the original price. If the price of a laptop is decreased by 10% to $360, then: $90\%\ of\ x = 360 \Rightarrow 0.90x = 360 \Rightarrow x = 360 \div 0.90 = 400$

25) Choice D is correct

Surface Area of a cylinder $= 2\pi r\ (r + h)$, The radius of the cylinder is 8 inches and its height is 12 inches. Surface Area of a cylinder $= 2\ (\pi)\ (8)\ (8 + 12) = 320\ \pi$

26) Choice D is correct

$average = \frac{sum\ of\ terms}{number\ of\ terms} \Rightarrow 18 = \frac{13+15+20+}{4} \Rightarrow 72 = 48 + x \Rightarrow x = 24$

27) Choice C is correct

Let x be the original price. If the price of the sofa is decreased by 25% to $420, then: $75\%\ of\ x = 420 \Rightarrow 0.75x = 420 \Rightarrow x = 420 \div 0.75 = 560$

28) Choice C is correct

Use simple interest formula: $I = prt$, (I = interest, p = principal, r = rate, t = time)

$I = (8,000)(0.045)(5) = 1,800$

29) Choice D is correct

$(4.2 \times 10^6) \times (2.6 \times 10^{-5}) = (4.2 \times 2.6) \times (10^6 \times 10^{-5}) = 10.92 \times (10^{6 + (-5)})$
$= 1.092 \times 10^2$

30) Choice D is correct

The formula of the volume of pyramid is: $V = \frac{l \times w \times h}{3}$. The length and width of the pyramid is $6\ cm$ and its height is $12\ cm$. Therefore: $V = \frac{6 \times 6 \times 12}{3} = 144\ cm^3$

"Effortless Math Education" Publications

Effortless Math authors' team strives to prepare and publish the best quality ASTB Mathematics learning resources to make learning Math easier for all. We hope that our publications help you learn Math in an effective way and prepare for the ASTB test.

We all in Effortless Math wish you good luck and successful studies!

Effortless Math Authors

www.EffortlessMath.com

... So Much More Online!

✓ FREE Math lessons

✓ More Math learning books!

✓ Mathematics Worksheets

✓ Online Math Tutors

Need a PDF version of this book?

Visit www.EffortlessMath.com

Made in the USA
Las Vegas, NV
22 February 2021